CREATIVE MOVEMENT FOR OLDER ADULTS

CREATIVE MOVEMENT FOR OLDER ADULTS
Exercises for the Fit to Frail

Pauline P. Fisher, M.A.

 HUMAN SCIENCES PRESS, INC.

Copyright © 1989 by Human Sciences Press, Inc.
A Subsidiary of Plenum Publishing Corporation
233 Spring Street, New York, N.Y. 10013

Printed in the United States of America

Library of Congress Cataloging in Publication Data

Fisher, Pauline P.
  Creative movement for older adults.

  Bibliography: p.
  Includes index.
  1. Aged—Health and hygiene.   2. Movement therapy.
I. Title.
RA777.6.F47   1988   613.7'04   88-13488
ISBN 0-89885-414-8

This book is dedicated to the memory of my father, Nathan Postiloff, who came to this country and persisted in making his dreams come true.

CONTENTS

FOREWORD

I first met Pauline Fisher in 1979 when I enrolled in her "Moving Experience" class. My motivation was dubious and my rationale somewhat selfish: to decrease stress. Being an individual who is rather cerebral, I found her classes to be curiously stimulating, invigorating and a catalyst for further pursuit of personal movement. I soon began taking classic ballet and jazz dance classes which I have now taken for nearly nine years.

Being a geriatrician, I was thrilled to find Pauline working with elders throughout the city and suburbs too. I personally observed her classes at a nursing home and on my Geriatric Unit. I realized that her techniques reached out to elders who sorely needed to move, feel good, and be with people.

Pauline's techniques for older adults emphasize the need for recognizing individuality in movement and other therapies. Rather than being rigid and structured, the techniques in this book allow each elder to find whatever movement feels good and safe—something akin to "environmental fit." Whether one can jeté or not is not the "pointe" in her class—moving a finger or a nod of the head may bring satisfaction and relief for an elder who has suffered a major stroke.

Pauline's classes stimulate blood circulation, increase stamina, increase socialization skills and, yes, decrease stress. I know you will find this book to be a fine resource for movement ideas.

Robert B. Vowels, M.D.
Director
Geriatric Rehabilitation Unit
District of Columbia General Hospital
Washington, DC

PREFACE

Like Shakespeare, I believe that "all the world's a stage" and that life is, as Baba Ram Dass (Richard Alpert) said, "The only dance there is." I find that if there's something you want to do, you may not do it; but if there's something you need to do, some way, some time, you will find the way to do it.

Dance was not something I wanted to do; it was something I had to do. Through dance one becomes more fully alive—physically, emotionally, intellectually, and spiritually. It opens a path toward one's higher self—a way to transcend the mundane.

As a result of my parents' discouragment, I wasn't able to begin formal dance training until age twelve. By the age of fifteen, I began teaching dance at a community center. My dance training has continued throughout my life and I came to realize later that life itself was, and continues to be, my greatest teacher.

It was as a dance education major that I entered Temple University in 1972. Then, because one of my sons had a learning disability, I began to explore the use of dance with learning-disabled students and other special children. This was the first exposure to the field of dance therapy. Later I became aware that I myself had learning differences and there seems no doubt that dance training helped a spatial disorientation.

The years in college opened exploration of meditation, yoga, the humanistic psychologies, theater improvisation, Tai Chi, creative visualization, body/mind theories, relaxation, and stress reduction techniques. I continued to teach ballet, modern dance, slimnastics, and creative movement education to children and adults, as well as to work with special populations; also, to develop the workshop program called "A Moving Experience."

These workshops explore the connection between body and mind; movement and emotions. They help people to better comprehend their personalities through the way in which they move, as well as to expand their movement vocabularies and improve awareness, awakening the child within through arts, play, and fun, while releasing joy.

In 1981 came an artist-in-residence grant from the Georgia Council for the Arts and Humanities. Although I had organized programs and performed for older adults in Pennsylvania during the 1960s, it was during that time in Georgia that I first experienced classes with older adults and found what a delight it was. The residency required the creation of new dances. One of those pieces, in memory of my grandmother, became the basis for "Particinformances."

Another special constituents grant was forthcoming from the D. C. Commission on the Arts and Humanities. This project was intergenerational, bringing together older adults and elementary schoolchildren. The older adults developed dance and interrelated arts performances with audience participation. They also facilitated workshops with the children.

Besides the work with older adults, I continue to work with others, including special populations, and have added stress reduction workshops for staff in nursing homes. By integrating education and life experience, I feel fortunate to be doing what I love, and enriched by the sharing of it.

ACKNOWLEDGMENTS

This book could not have been written without the knowledge and inspiration I received from all the teachers and others from whom I have learned. To Meli Davis Kaye, my appreciation for stretching my experience and exposure to Dance and the Arts.

I give thanks to all of my students who helped me develop into the teacher I am today. I especially thank all my classes of older adults whose photos and stories help to make up this book.

To David Sparkman, my friend, who helped with editing and advice on the original manuscript goes my deepest gratitude for his time, patience, and moral support.

I also want to thank my friend, Renya Craig, for her spiritual support and her generosity with time for the final typing of this book.

To my special friend, Mark, for his moral support and giving nature, I give thanks.

My appreciation to Paul Elliot for his suggestions and advice.

A special thanks to Marsha and Marvin for their hideaway on the beach when I needed a peaceful place to write.

And to all of my family and friends who encouraged me and believed in me. I thank you.

Chapter 1

INTRODUCTION AND BEGINNING

More Than Movement is a program I use with older adults and other special populations ranging in physical condition from the very fit to the very frail. My main goal is to get people moving in whatever way they can while they are having fun and learning that whatever they can do, *can* be dance. At the same time they are becoming more aware of their bodies and themselves. Using my knowledge of dance and other arts, my life's experiences and sensitivity, I vary my approach and focus depending upon the needs of each group, be they physically, mentally, or emotionally handicapped, gifted and talented, children or older adults.

Not only do I take the body into consideration, but I include the emotions, how people feel, as well as the intellect, bringing in ideas to think about or new information. I also strongly believe in a higher force that guides our spiritual selves. For some this aspect may be uncomfortable, but I find that the people in my classes respond to and appreciate the inclusion and recognition of this part of themselves.

As noted in *Aging Network News:* "A 1982 Gallup report on Religion in America stated that 76 percent of respondents between the ages of 50 to 64 felt that religion was the most important influence in their lives; 87 percent of those 65 and older also felt religion was important to them."[1]

Another article from the same publication states that "spiritual well-being is an affirmation of life in a relationship with God, one's self, community and environment."[2]

In comparing this program to other movement and exercise programs they experienced, comments from class members noted that my program included all participants, and allowed each to work at his/her own level, capability, and comfort. Others said there was more concern for the individual, more creativity, more activity than in other classes, and more of a body and mind connection. The following quotes are from some of the participants from my program at the Oakcrest Apartment Complex after being asked what they had gained from the program:

"I've learned to relax, I've developed muscles and lost weight and I now do exercises every day for 15 minutes."—Gwen Verdi

"I look forward to each session; I laugh a lot and have enjoyed all the classes immensely."—Marie Palmer

"I have come to all the classes and it has been a wonderful help in learning to relax. I have enjoyed myself, met nice people and now move more quickly."—Kitty Puleo

"Increased interest in exercise and diet, more body and health consciousness and it has added to my personal daily exercises."—Cathy Railsback

Rev. Steven Carr, a member of the group at the Evelyn I. Cole Multi-purpose Senior Center, and a stroke victim, said he gained more from my class than all the physical therapy he has had, because it was more fun and because of the encouragement from the others in the group. Often people who come in and say, "I can't do anything today, I'm not feeling well," will forget about themselves and get totally involved in the activities.

More Than Movement includes movement and dance, music, art, imagery, deep breathing and relaxation techniques, sensitivity awareness, theater games, imaginative activities to initiate movement, communication motivators, and memory reinforcements. All the activities are enjoyable, creative processes. Participants gain self-confidence while exploring new skills, or old skills in new ways.

The goals of this program are to:

Enhance joint articulation and body image as well as enjoyment of body movement.

Improve balance, flexibility, and strength.

Enhance awareness through developing perceptual skills and reawakening the senses.

Acquire techniques for relaxation and stress management.

Achieve deeper and more conscious breathing.

Awaken creative ability.

Learn motivators for memory reinforcement, communication skills, and develop easier social interactions.

Have fun and laugh.

One of the staff at a hospital geriatric unit said, "Your activities help the patients pull themselves out of themselves." If they are participating in any way, then they are being aware of what is happening. In settings such as these I find everyone responds to music, and the variety of the activities I bring in is a key issue for attracting attention and interest.

It is important to note that when working with the

confused, Alzheimer or dementia individuals they will not remember from time to time.

Try to be as flexible and patient as you can and be aware that conditions may often be less than optimal. In my experience I have had to hold classes in situations such as:

A retirement apartment complex where we met in an open space next to the lobby, which could be looked upon as either beneficial (some of those passing through became interested and joined the group) or not (some in the group felt self-conscious being watched).

Wards of hospitals or state nursing homes where the loudspeaker periodically interrupted our class.

The activity room of an apartment complex, where it was often too hot or too cold, and many times the door was locked, which meant finding a maintenance man to get the door opened.

A recreation and nutrition center where there was only one large area, our class was held in the midst of the activities of another group, and lunch was often being set up.

In many nursing homes or resident centers there are only soft couches and chairs that you sink into—phones may be ringing, visitors or other residents may be coming in and out.

A fire drill may disrupt your class.

Some state facilities are understaffed so you may need to gather the patients together yourself.

I remember in the ward of one place I worked, the stench of urine was strong and the nurses wheeled in sleeping seniors. But once I got started I forgot about the stench. I was able to awaken and stimulate most of the people, and the majority participated. They thanked me for coming and said they hoped I would return.

Remember that:

Many have hearing difficulties—so speak up.

Some have visual impairment, so you may need to demonstrate at close range.

Not all individuals will be dressed comfortably or properly for free movement and exercise. (The female residents of one retirement home came dressed every time in dresses, girdles, stockings, and heels and wouldn't think of dressing otherwise.)

The very confused may ramble on, give incoherent or inappropriate responses; some may try to put props or textures in their mouth. One woman tried to open a tambourine as if it were a cookie can. Another asked if the bus was coming.

The energy level is lower in the afternoons.

With the very frail or very confused go slow and have no expectations—RELAX!

When I first started working in a state nursing home I felt as if the environment was a vacuum. After two weeks my goals changed. I was now there to: stimulate, get responses, awaken, give whatever moments of joy, aliveness, awareness, as were possible.

It is my belief that anyone who cares about people and is sensitive to individual needs and abilities has the credentials that can guide them in working with special people. Before beginning take a deep breath, tune into your heart, and remember to be flexible and to have fun. Enthusiasm for what you're doing is contagious and makes a difference to those you're working with.

When presenting this material it is a good idea to feel comfortable with your own body. Choose activities that you enjoy doing. If you approach fitness as a chore, as a medicine that has to be taken to feel better rather than fun that feels good, or as an activity to fill time and keep a group occupied, this attitude will be projected and felt and the response from the group more than likely will be likewise. Be honest with yourself and the group, believe in what you are doing and be able to do it yourself. And don't be afraid of trying something new.

Be sure to give praise during the class. Reassure the participants with compliments without being patronizing. Move around the room occasionally. Go to those who need assistance with an activity, either directing or moving their bodies gently or placing their arms, or other body parts correctly for them.

Before beginning a new class I tell everyone to do only what feels right for them, to pay attention to their own body's abilities. I say, "We're here for pleasure, not pain."

MUSICAL INSTRUMENTS—RHYTHM SOUNDS AND GROUP ECHO

I begin most of my classes by passing around a musical instrument. If it is an unusual one, I talk about it first, explaining to the group that even if I don't know how to play it, I can play with it. I ask each person to do whatever they'd like on the instrument and then to say their name. This activity is fun and helps to bring the class together. Most people don't get the opportunity to experience musical instruments personally—to make sounds themselves and to hear the immediate sound feedback. This is gratifying and often provokes joyous smiles. Saying our names is a way of saying "Hi, this is me and I'm here" and it also reminds us of, and reinforces, all the names in the group.

A variation on this is for each person to do a rhythm and for the group to echo by clapping it back. The rhythm can be one of the individual's own design. If someone has difficulty, I suggest that person try using the rhythm (by syllables) of their full name or their birth date. For example, Mary Ann Patterson has six beats and the rhythm would be as it is said: -- - ---. An accent can be placed anywhere. Some of these can be put together into a song and then movement can be added. If desired, this process could be developed further.

My collection of musical instruments include a tambourine, a variety of drums, such as a tongue drum and a steel drum, cymbals, a thumb piano, chimes, bells, a home-made bass, a limber jack, and more. I am always on the lookout for interesting instruments that anyone can play with, and I add to my collection whenever I can. However, when instruments are not available, you can either make your own, using keys to shake, a coffee can as a tom-tom, or even beans in a jar. You can also make body sounds such as clap, stamp your feet, pat your thighs or click your tongue.

Deep Breathing and Breath Awareness—Bubbles, Candle Flame, Pinwheel, and Balloons

A class also can start with deep breathing. Deep breathing and breath awareness can be facilitated by blowing soap bubbles, blowing out the flame of a candle, blowing enough to make a pinwheel spin, and/or blowing a balloon off someone's hand. Each of these call for a different kind of breath, such as slow and long, or short and fast. Deep breathing brings oxygen to the lungs and helps activate the diaphragm, which in turn helps take in more oxygen. In this way the lungs get rid of carbon dioxide and other waste products. This process helps you feel better.

Soap Bubbles

Soap bubbles are both pretty and fun. One older adult asked me if I had ever blown soap bubbles in freezing weather, claiming that they freeze. Quite often a member

Figure 1-1   Blowing and Breaking Soap Bubbles

of the group who rarely participates in other activities will blow the bubbles.

This activity calls for a long slow breath. For some very frail this may be difficult. I extend this activity by using music and having each person break the bubbles with different parts of their body. For those who can, I have one person blow the bubbles while another dances the bubbles away, breaking them with as many body parts as possible, using their legs and head as well as elbows and feet. The music and bubbles motivate the other group members to cheer on those participating.

In another variation each participant holds the applicator in one hand, makes large arm movements that will blow the bubbles around, and then changes hands and repeats. Music can motivate more dancelike movement.

This stimulates body part articulation and movement

that is fun and more like dance than exercise. Although the attention is on breaking the bubbles, each person is moving and loosening muscles that may be stiff in their own way and at their own speed.

Candle Flame

Bring a candle in a holder to class. Light the candle for each person, asking each to make a wish before blowing out the candle. This takes a short and hard breath and some very frail may need assistance.

This activity could be extended into a memory recaller by asking if anyone remembers the first birthday candles they blew out, or other times in their lives that they blew out a candle flame. Not only will this motivate sharing and communication, but it may aid memory function.

Figure 1-2   Pinwheels

Pinwheels

Pinwheels can be introduced for a long and strong breath. Pinwheels are pretty and attract attention when they spin. Often the group may have to be reminded that they must blow into one of the pockets to get the pinwheel to spin and you may need to point out the pocket. Another activity with the pinwheel is to have each person stand, when possible, and dance as they move the pinwheel through space with each arm in turn used to make it spin.

Balloons

Have each participant blow a balloon off your hand as you hold it near their mouth. If each person tilts his or her head toward the ceiling and you hold the balloon *very* gently between your hands over the person's mouth, the balloon can be blown up towards the ceiling.

The following are variations of balloon activities.

Catch and Toss

For the very frail as well as the fit it is fun to catch and throw a balloon. They are light and fairly easy to catch, although sometimes they can be rather evasive. This also gives each person the opportunity to work one-on-one with the leader. After each has had a chance to catch and throw three times, I then ask them to hit it back to me three times by either slapping or punching it. For some confused individuals, they may be able to just do one or the other (catch or hit). Any response is acceptable because it means an attempt is being made to pay attention and to participate.

In one of the nursing homes there was a woman who never responded to anything. She seemed to live in her own world. She was brought to the group each time in her

Figure 1-3   Balloons, Catch and Toss

wheelchair. During our introductions with musical instruments, I would play for her and say her name. One day when we were doing balloon tosses, I took the chance of tossing it to her after asking her if she'd like to catch it. Much to my surprise she caught it. It may have been an automatic response, but it was a response. Since then I have become aware of her apparent attention (her gaze and head turn) at other activities as well.

Kick the Balloon

Give each person a balloon and a Magic Marker and let them put their name, a design, or a mark of their own on the balloon.

For the very frail the balloon may be placed at each person's feet to be kicked a few times with each foot. They also may attempt to kick it up in the air or to another person.

For the fit it is fun to stand in a circle and kick the balloon to another person, even using more than one balloon to build the excitement. In a mixed group where there are some who cannot stand easily—or at all—those who can stand form the circle with those in the chairs included.

Another variation for a fit group is to make a standing circle and try to keep one or more balloons in the air, first with just hands and then with other body parts hitting the balloon. I usually begin with one balloon and, one at a time, add others until there are three or four, depending upon the group. This activity generates a lot of positive energy and motivates much movement and laughter.

CATEGORY DANCES

Name with Movement

A good way to start with a new group is with an activity that uses movement that gives each participant the opportunity to present themselves by stating their names. Ask each member of the group to say their first name and, depending upon the group and their physical capability, do a body part or whole body movement at the same time. Each person repeats their name and movement, and then the entire group does it with them twice, as best they can. As with the musical instrument introduction, this activity helps reinforce names for both the facilitator and the group members. It gives each person a chance to see how their own movement looks on other people as well as to see variations of their creation.

It is essential to accept all variations, to set up an environment that says, "You're okay, whatever you do is acceptable, you can be creative." If an individual feels vulnerable or intimidated and has taken a risk by presenting themselves with their own movement, acceptance gives the feeling of success. Therefore, the class time becomes a safe place to be—to be yourself, to be silly, to experiment creatively, to express yourself.

Things for all to be aware of are: 1) how different the movement may look compared to the person's perception of how it felt and vice versa; and 2) how each person's movement reflects their personality or mood.

Depending upon the number of people in each group and their capacity for remembering, these movements—or some of them—can be strung together into a dance. In order to help to develop this dance into a presentation or part of a larger performance production, add music, variations of each movement, transitions between each, and staging (placing the bodies in a form or changing formations.)

Body Part Warm-Ups and Dances

Exercises are most often done in a technique form, but an alternative to this can be a body part dance created by the participants. When members of the group are unable to propose movements, the facilitator can guide the group by asking each member of the group for a movement of a specific body part resulting in a dance that includes the body from head to toe. For example, the facilitator can ask the first person to give a head movement and the next person a shoulder movement. Continue this process until you have worked down to the feet, going back to the beginning each time after another movement has been added. Do each movement four times.

Repeating the dance as you are developing it is good exercise in itself. When you have completed this process, put the whole thing together with fast upbeat music and "dance it." Music with a distinct beat, such as disco, helps greatly. This whole dance can then be repeated in slow motion to similarly appropriate music.

Other dances can be developed from any category, such as sports, birthday or other parties, a walk in the park, a picnic, or a visit to the beach. An example of how one of these might develop is to pick a category such as "A Day on the Beach" and then ask the members to suggest things we do at the beach. When necessary, help or add to these ideas (e.g., put on suntan lotion, swim, play volleyball, people-watch, soak up the sun, build sand castles, take a walk, or look for seashells). At each suggestion, have the group do it in movement and start from the beginning as you add each new movement, put to music or sound effects. The "dance" can be done in a sitting position or, for a more mobile and active group, the "dance" can move across the floor or through space.

MUSIC SELECTION

Music selection is an important part of my program. I try to start with music that each group can relate to, such as music from their cultural background or music that was popular in their earlier years. From that point I add a variety of music, introducing new musical selections to expand the musical knowledge of each group. I feel it enhances each activity to accompany it with music that heightens the experience.

INTERGENERATIONAL

We, or our societal structures, often isolate ourselves into categorized groups, such as by age or handicap, race or cultural background. In some areas this has changed somewhat. Today there is more mainstreaming of children with handicaps, or physically, mentally, or emotionally challenged children, which is the preferential label now, into regular schools; and there is a growing interest in intergenerational programs, programs that bring together different generations. I have been involved with one that brought teenagers together with older adults for fitness and relaxation and another that brought preschoolers together with older adults for creative dance and exercise. Both of these were successful. I am now planning an in-

Figure 1-4   Intergenerational

tergenerational program with hearing impaired older adults and hearing impaired children.

I believe we need to do more of this to dispel the stereotypical beliefs of each group about the other and to bring together the joy and verve of the very young with the wealth of knowledge of the other, and the abundance of love both have to give and share.

Many of my techniques have been derived from my work with children which I have been able to vary and translate for all ages. Many of the activities in this book can be used to bring generations of ages together for fun and sharing as well as learning.

Chapter 2

MORE DANCES

After the class has come together in whatever method you have chosen (passing a musical instrument around, clapping names, etc.), done some deep breathing and a general body part warm-up, the rest of your time together can be shared using one or many of the following creative processes. Some can be repeated whenever appropriate, or extended and developed over time.

Those who are in the room but outside the circle, or who come to the group and do not participate, will still enjoy themselves just by being there; laughing with the group or listening to the music.

When someone comes into a group and says, "I'm not feeling well, I'm just going to watch," they just as often find themselves participating. I remember when at a retirement home a woman said, "I am extremely dizzy and have a headache. Can I just come and watch?" She eventually forgot her dizziness and headache and ended up participating fully. The color in her face changed and so did her energy. Not only did the activity help her, but simply leaving her room where she was alone and joining the others proved beneficial also.

It is the responsibility of the leader to keep the energy level up, especially with older adults who are in pain or depressed. When I was teaching at a hospital geriatric unit, one man confined to a wheelchair was wheeled in and angrily said he was in pain and wasn't going to move. But once the group got started, he forgot his pain and found himself involved in the activities. Later he said he had enjoyed himself, which I had already observed by the change in his expression and the way in which he joined in. After another session at a nursing home, a nurse exclaimed, "That was great! Your enthusiasm even makes me feel better."

At one state nursing home where I worked a few people were sometimes obstinate, but when I joked with them they softened and joked back with me. When I asked one man if he'd tell me his name and he barked, "No, I won't!" I jumped back and overacted, saying I'd tell him mine anyway, and he laughed and told me his. We were like two young children playing.

When I teach I am totally involved in what I'm doing and the people I'm with. I am in the moment. I'm comfortable with myself, with what I'm doing and with the group. It is natural for me to remain continually relaxed yet active. Without being frantic or overexcited, I maintain a stimulated, attentive attitude. Giving of myself comes across; I end up infecting others with my energy. Even when I sometimes feel tired or low before teaching, once I start to teach—giving and receiving—I am uplifted. No matter what is going on in my life, I enter my classes with a positive attitude. Like an actress going onstage, once I enter a class I have changed roles. However, I am not acting, I am that person. I have refocused my thoughts and I enter dancing.

Remember, energy creates more energy—a good

mood is transmitted. There are times, however, when things that are askew in my life are strongly on my mind. In such cases I simply share my feelings so that we can look at the similarities in our humanness. I end up looking at my own problems from a distance. Sometimes we can laugh together at ourselves. It is important to be honest and not patronizing.

These times are stimulating and help the group to become more socially interactive. Internal motivation aids physical interaction and increases the energy level. When verbal interaction occurs it is easier to get people moving more. This also works in the reverse. After a movement class there is more sharing and communicating. When there is more physical action, people are more animated and the reverse is just as true.

It is a good idea to try and do each of the activities as you read them, to experience them in your body and not just in your head.

EMOTION/MOTION

Many older adults often do not have the opportunity to discuss emotions, particularly feelings that may be specific to aging. Given the permission to share these feelings in a safe environment with a group of their peers is a freeing experience. Being able to "dance" these emotions can release tension relating to specific emotions that may be stored in the body.

Holding and tightening the body is a result of blocking expressions of feeling. Therefore, suppressed emotion will eventually affect body movement. Chronic muscular tension can affect full breathing and result in binding energy. Wilhelm Reich referred to this muscular tension as *armoring*. Wherever this chronic tension is held in the body, it looks and feels like an armor plate.

In his book, *Bioenergetics*, Alexander Lowen gives the

following examples of how these muscle tensions may begin: ". . . One inhibits the impulse to cry by setting the jaw, constricting the throat, holding the breath and tightening the belly. Anger as expressed in striking out can be inhibited by contracting the muscles of the shoulder girdle, thereby pulling the shoulders back . . ." (p. 144).

Expressing, sharing, and moving together can ease the sense of isolation and related emotions that older adults may often feel. Moving with others helps the individual move through these emotions. Intense or negative feelings may emerge, but these permit the group to discuss old emotions as well as present ones. At one retirement home where I worked this activity opened a discussion about death. Another time, the death of a group member precipitated a discussion of fate and acceptance. Upon arriving for a class I was informed of the untimely death of one of the members of the group. She had been run over by a car the day before. After listening to the details, I told a story about a time when I had been riding my bike and another biker was coming towards me from the opposite direction on a collision course. I veered to the other side and at the same time so did she. Once again I veered back and so did she. I anxiously tried to avoid this collision, but no matter what I did it seemed inevitable; and so it was. Fortunately neither of us got badly hurt, but it reminded me that some things in life are unavoidable, as if they are meant to be. Although both my body and pride were slightly bruised, the accident served as a reason to remind me about acceptance.

REPETITION MOVEMENT

Choose an emotion after discussing several in the group. Discuss some emotions they have seen in television or movies. Share times you've experienced a specific emotion or one you've seen expressed by others, such as happiness, joy, anger, frustration, pain, fear, impatience, love, etc. Ask the group to offer movement that expresses a particular emotion. This is done by having someone or the whole group do a movement that expresses each suggested emotion. Then do a follow-the-leader, allowing each person to lead with their own movement, one at a time, so that each person in the group may experience this movement in his or her own body. Repeat each movement several times.

An example would be for the first person to shake her fists in anger and everyone would follow. The next person in the circle would continue with the same emotion by perhaps stamping her feet and after everyone repeated this the next person might bring her fist down on her thigh and shout, "NO!"

Remind everyone to be aware of feelings that may emerge from the movement and tell them to observe how the others look as they do each emotion/motion.

STATUES

Do a small group statue expressing each emotion. A group statue is formed when each person, one at a time, does a movement position and freezes in a pose. The first person starts in the center and each person does their own pose to express the same emotions. This also can be done by using all the movements, one by one, that express one particular emotion. Attach each person to another by having each doing a different movement, still expressing the same emotion, connecting their bodies in some manner. For example, a shoulder could connect to a hip, a hand touching a toe, or a back, etc.

Each statue can be done in a different way. One statue can move in a breathing fashion, contracting and expanding. The group moves as one, expanding out or up together while still maintaining the connections, as if the group were the statue taking a breath. Then the entire group moves in or down together, as if it were breathing out and contracting or deflating, while still maintaining the connection.

Another statue can be created by moving body parts. Three or four people join together, standing or remaining in their chairs, all doing their own movements expressing a single chosen emotion. The group arranges their bodies so that they form one statue by the way their bodies face or connect. Statues can be done with small or large groups. Music or sounds also may be added.

The statue activity can be expanded from emotions to categories with an emotional content, such as war, family, the cosmos, storms at sea, frolicking on the beach, etc.

This activity and the following two allow for creatively expressing emotions as well as creative development of a tableau or dance. At the same time, the movements created are stretching, bending and twisting the body, providing the opportunity for creative exercise.

DANCES

Ask each person to do something with their bodies and also to make sounds, if they wish, to express a specific emotion. If, for instance, a happy dance has been decided upon, the first person might jump up for joy, arms waving and shout, "Yippie!" The second person might clap her hands gleefully, the third might decide to sit and laugh out loud, spreading the arms up and out as the body leans back and then bends forward to slap the thighs while still laughing, and so on, until all present have added happy movements.

After each movement is contributed, start from the beginning once again, reinforcing and rehearsing as you string the movements together to form the dance. One person at a time, or the entire group, can do each movement in succession. This dance can be repeated many times and may be added to.

In one of the groups I work with, a laughing movement was done by a participant and each time the group performed the dance, this laughing movement sparked waves of contagious, invigorating laughter.

When I asked the members of this class to express their feelings on this, I received some of the following responses: "You feel happy. It relaxes you, releases tension. When I laugh, I cry and it seems to rinse and cleanse the whole body; it washes away pent-up emotions. It helps you forget your problems. It's contagious and cheers you up. It releases energy."

The composition of the dance may be changed by changing the timing, i.e., starting fast with an emotion such as anger and slowing it down with each repetition in order to intensify the presentation of that emotion. Or, starting with an emotion such as joy, you may begin in slow motion and, with each repetition, speed up movements until they are being done quickly. Members of the group also may have more ideas for variations.

Another good way to structure a dance is to have three different movements that represent the same emotions done simultaneously by groups of three or four.

Adding props and costumes or costume touches such as scarves, ribbons, or masks, works to enhance the intensity of the dance. Masks could be made by the members of the group as an added project, or a high school art class could be invited to design and make them for the group.

STORY FORMS

Dances can be woven into making a complete story by using past experiences or making up the story as you go along. As an example, take the experiences shared during the discussion of specific emotions experienced or seen in others and have the group express and weave these into a story.

A poem, short story, or fairy tale may be chosen to make a dance just as well.

Dances and story forms allow you to add elements derived from other arts: music, drama, visual arts, costume making, and poetry. This stimulates the different talents in each individual to emerge.

The following activity, called Hand Dance, is a somewhat more intimate activity, in which individuals in the group relate to one another. It helps members of the group get to know each other in a different way. Not only is there touch in a sensitive, quiet way, but there is playful touch as well as increased opportunity for eye contact. It should also be pointed out during the exercise, and in the discussion afterword, how the emotions and the personality are reflected in our movements.

HAND DANCE WITH PARTNER

I choose to introduce this activity when the group has been meeting for some time and is comfortable with the leader and with each other. This exercise is not appropriate with the frail elderly.

The entire activity is done silently; only the body speaks. Laughter and sounds are, of course, perfectly fine. Allow sufficient time after giving each instruction to allow the group to fully explore. Tell the group: "Find a partner. Place your chairs so that you are facing each other and are close enough to place your hands and your partner's hands together, palms touching, fingers facing up. Close your eyes and just breath deeply, concentrating on the warmth and touch of you and your partner's hands."

After approximately one minute, say, "Open your eyes

and allow your hands to separate to the point of almost touching, maintaining an awareness of the warmth between you. Try the next part, occasionally closing the eyes. Try separating your hands a bit more and then let your hands move to and from your partner, experiencing the points at which you no longer feel the warmth of your partner's hands." Some may be able to experience what feels like a magnetic pull.

Hello

Next, tell the group: "Keep your eyes open as you find ways to say hello with your hands, working through the clichéd movements such as a hand wave, a pat on the hand, and shaking hands. Try to explore the temperature, warmth, and coolness of different parts of the hands. Feel and see the variations of color—under the nails, knuckles, veins, blemishes, freckles, and scars. Get to know each other through the hands. Explore different pressures, such as light and firm touches and smoothly running fingers along the fingers and hands."

The leader must be sensitive to the group and change to the next step when appropriate.

Dance

Continue with the following instructions to the group: "When you are ready, make a transition to a playful and creative dance. Find a way to dance with your hands and your partner's, as if they were puppets on a stage. Try following each other and taking off on your own dance, then returning to your partner's hands. Sometimes, if and when you'd like, touch, and sometimes not." Ask everyone to: "*Freeze,* and take note of your body posture." Suggest some questions they might pose to themselves while in this frozen position: "Are you leaning towards or away from your partner? Where are you loose or tense or tight? Is your back curved or straight? Are your fingers curled or in fists? Are your elbows and arms out and away from your body or close to your body? How are your feet making contact? Where is your focus?

Remind the group to: "Just take note, do not judge. Be aware and be conscious." After these suggested questions, tell them to go back to the dance, remembering that they are still not verbalizing (speaking).

Fight

Inform the group: "When you are ready, switch to a mock fight, using all your power. A mock fight is a fight mimicked in play. 'Get into it.' Allow yourself to make sounds, if you like. Grunt and groan."

When the group has been at this for a few minutes, or whenever you feel the timing is right, have them freeze once more. Once again ask them to notice their body positions. Remind them to ask themselves these questions: "How is your body different from the last freeze? Have you used more of your body? Are you closer to or further from your partner? Now where are you curved or straight? Ask yourself some of the same questions as the last time you froze your position. How do you feel both physically and emotionally? When you are ready, go back to the fighting for a minute or so."

Make Up

When you feel the group is ready, tell them to find ways to ask for forgiveness with their hands.

Farewell

When you feel the group has had sufficient time to make up tell them to find a way, also using their hands, to say farewell. When they have let go of the physical contact, tell them to make eye contact for ten seconds.

Have the group come together and share their experiences and feelings. Some questions you may want them to respond to are: "Did you feel comfortable at first with your partner? Did you find new ways to say hello? Do you feel closer with your partner now? Did you find yourself dancing alone or together during the dance sequence with your partner? Did you have touch contact or did you dance alone?"

Also: "How did you feel during the fight? Was it fun? Scary? Uncomfortable? How do you usually feel during an argument or confrontation? Did you 'get into it' or avoid it? Were you wrestling or hitting? What did you discover during the freezes? How do you usually say good-bye? How did it feel? How did the eye contact feel?" Feel free to think up other questions.

After you have asked these questions and allowed a minute or so for the group to think about them and perhaps answer them in their own minds, then select a few of these or other questions and allow each person to respond. Let each person verbalize their own feelings and perceptions.

CHARLESTON AND OTHER DANCES—"SHALL WE DANCE?"

The Charleston and other dances can be done in chairs or standing, according to the ability of the participants. I have found that we can have as much fun dancing in our chairs. I have taught the Charleston, waltz, and simple shuffle-tap-step dance as well as the cancan in a sitting position. For those who can and want to try, we do the dances standing. For those who remain in their chairs dancing, I come and dance with each of them. I stand, hold their hands as we dance, letting them experience the flow of the

Figure 2-1 Charleston

movement and music. The kinesthetic (muscle) movement brings a glow to their faces and often the rest of their bodies sway in rhythm to the music. You can feel them dancing inside their bodies. They *are* dancing!

During a demonstration in a class at a retirement home a very frail woman said, "I can't move." I said, "Sure you can, how about if I move with you?" With her permission I took her arms gently and we moved together. Slowly our arms made larger and larger movements. A smile came to her face as she obviously enjoyed the sense of moving safely.

With a very frail population I may end my classes dancing with each person in this manner. It may be anything from a disco to a cha-cha to a waltz. This gives us the chance for eye contact, personal contact (touch), and a shared movement experience, as well as a feeling of closure to the session.

One time when I was on tour in Illinois I danced in this manner with a woman in a wheelchair. While I was holding her hands, we moved joyously in rhythm to the music and she stood up. Later I found out that she had not stood in three years, due to extremely painful arthritis. In the excitement of the moment and the involvement with the music and dance, she stood.

Chapter 3

ELEMENTS OF MOVEMENT

The elements of movement are part of the vocabulary of dance. Just as baking and cooking have ingredients that make up each of the recipes, movement components are the ingredients that make up dances. Shape, space, time, and force are used by dancers, artists, and musicians alike. In dance and movement we also use locomotor and non-locomotor movements, and what I call *energies*.

It is important for each person who leads a group to decide whether the activities are appropriate for their group. Since each group is as individual as each person, it is best for the facilitators to choose and perhaps vary the activities for their particular groups. In this book I will sometimes state when an activity is not appropriate for a frail group; but often a group may be mixed in abilities, both physically and mentally, so it is up to each teacher to decide what to use and how. I have worked with some groups where all are frail, some of whom all are confused, and some that are mixed, as well as some groups who are all both physically and mentally alert and active.

SHAPE, SPACE, TIME, AND FORCE[3]

Shape is the position the body or any body part takes in space. Shape can be explored in the following ways:

> Make a shape with a specific body part, such as an arm or leg.
>
> Make a shape with the whole body—first, in a frozen pose; then find a way to move in this pose, either in place or through space (around the room).
>
> Have a leader call out two or three body parts with which each participant can make a statue (frozen pose) or move in space.
>
> Make a set of cards with names and possibly photos from magazines of various body parts. Have someone in the group pick a card which will determine the body part that they will then touch to another body part.

For instance, if a card with the word or picture of a nose is chosen, tell them: "You must walk around the room and touch the walls with your nose or touch everyone's nose." Or they may partner-up and touch each other's noses. If two cards are picked, they may try to touch one part to the other, such as touching a nose to a knee, if they can, or touching a knee to another person's knee. This game can be varied in many ways.

> Make a shape with a body part and trace it on a piece of paper.
>
> Find a way of making shadows and make shadow shapes with body parts or the whole body.

In partners, first one makes a shape with the whole body and then, at a signal, the other partner makes a shape while the first relaxes.

Space includes:

1. *Path* of movement—straight (direct) or curved, twisted, and crooked (indirect, flexible). Path is the road you travel, as Dorothy travelled the yellow brick road in *The Wizard of Oz*.
2. *Direction* is the way the body is moving, such as forward, backward, sideways, diagonally, turning in, out, up, and down.
3. *Level* is the position of the body, such as prone, sitting, squatting, kneeling, standing, or elevated, so that it can be low, middle, or high.
4. *Size* of the movement might be large, tall, wide, small, short, low, or narrow.
5. *Focus* is where the eyes look—constant in a particular direction, wandering, near, far, outward, or inward.

I suggest that you make a stack of cards for each of these so that you may mix these ingredients and make your own 'recipes' (i.e., mix the elements to design your own activities). Here are a few of my ideas:

Choose some element of space for each body part to explore. For example, move elbows in the *directions* of front and back. Then do a large and high movement with an arm, exploring *size*. Follow this with a movement on a low *level* in a straight *path* while keeping the *focus* wandering, as if watching a butterfly fluttering around while crawling on your hands and knees.

Split the group in half or have the group in partners facing each other. Choose two *directions*, such as back and front, and a *path*, such as straight. Have half the group use their legs and the other half use their arms and ask them to explore dancing in these directions and this path with the chosen body parts; then have the groups change body parts.

Level and *path* can be explored by calling out a path and, at a signal, changing levels while continuing along the same path. At another signal, change the path while maintaining the same level. For instance, the leader can ask the group to walk a straight path and, at the beat of a drum or the clap of the leader's hands, walk on tiptoes, or with knees bent. Or tell the group to walk a straight path while moving a body part in a curved pattern.

For those who can't walk, a straight path can be explored with an arm on a low level and then a high level.

Focus can be explored by having a group leader or, if in partners, one partner hold an object and move the object so the eyes follow. Or make a script: "Look at the table, the painting on the back wall, the floor near your foot and out the windows." Tell the group to walk with focus wandering, with focus far away, with the focus inward and then straight ahead.

Time can be changed by the rate of speed (tempo) of movement—from slow to fast. Dividing the period between pulse beats into even or uneven parts is another way that time can be changed.

Many activities can be explored or varied by changing the element of time. Music can be used to initiate this change. Dances can be set to a specific number of beats and then varied by changing the invervals between the beats.

The following are some examples of how you can get the group to do this. Tell them:

> "Walk around the room three times. First very slowly, then a bit faster, and then as fast as you can."
> "Move your arms in a circular path (pattern) very

quickly and, at a signal, change to moving them in slow motion."

"Walk while keeping time with a 4/4 beat (- - - -). After four sets, change to four sets of a 5/4 beat (-- ---). This is the rhythm of a cha-cha dance.

Force (dynamics) may be described as movement that is tense, heavy, hard, relaxed, soft, light, or weak.

In order for the group to explore each of these, ask them to walk around the room, starting with a normal walk. Tell them that at a given signal everyone will stop. Then you call out, "Walk *tensed*." Again, at a predetermined signal, everyone will stop and you can then call out, "Walk *heavily*." This process can continue until all of the elements of force have been explored. You may decide to explore just two each time you do this activity.

Another way to explore force would be to do a movement with a specific body part. Then choose a specific force and repeat the movement with that force. For instance, you could say: "Swing your arms front and back naturally, and then swing them heavily, as if each weighed a ton."

ENERGIES

This is a term I use to describe movement done to the musical terms legato, staccato, vibratory, swinging and percussive. After discussing each of these, one at a time, giving examples in visual images, sounds, and music, I ask the group to explore each with individual body parts and then ask them to move the whole body in this energy. I also ask the group to pick a partner and have a short conversation using the voice in the type of energy that is being explored.

Legato is constant, even-flowing movement. It is usually done in slower motion because it is more difficult to control when done fast. There are no jerky movements in legato, and they are usually rounded and curved. Examples of visual images are: flowing water, the movement of wheat in a field, and astronauts in outer space.

Staccato is short, fast, jerky movement, like touching a hot iron or clapping your hands. Staccato movement is usually angular and sharp. It can be even or uneven in rhythm. The lines on a lined sheet of paper or a visual repetition of any pattern are visual examples of staccato. A Gene Davis stripe painting is a good example of a staccato pattern. Jazz and disco music are staccato and the sound of a train rolling across tracks is an example of staccato sound. Authoritarian voices, such as military orders, "March, hut 2,3,4, about face!" and reprimanding, such as, "Don't you ever do that again!" accompanied by a pointing and shaking finger, would be staccato voices. Richard Nixon's voice is staccato.

Vibratory. There is a fine line between staccato and vibratory. The latter is much quicker. It is like shivering and rapid shaking, such as when someone is very cold or very nervous. The movement can be tense or loose. A jackhammer is a good example of a vibratory sound.

This is a difficult energy for most people to sustain and, therefore, may not be comfortable to do for as long as the other energies.

Swinging is just that, like being on a swing, like a pendulum. It is a giving into gravity and suspending briefly in the air before falling back again. This is best explored by having everyone lift an arm in the air and letting that arm fall in a swinging arc until it comes to a stop and suspends, before letting it fall and return again in an arc. This can be done with a feeling of falling and giving into gravity, or with force, as if throwing the arm away or pitching a baseball underhand. Continual swinging movement often becomes circular. Scalloped edges and spirals are visual images of swinging. Waltz music is swinging. The stereotypical voice of a Southern belle or a whining child would be examples of voices that dip up and down in a swinging rhythm.

Percussive is explosive, like being shot out of a cannon, or a firecracker going off. It is like a karate chop, quick and strong—like going through a wall. Much of the music of the composers Béla Bartók and Darius Milhaud, for example, is percussive.

Have the group explore each energy, one at a time; first, all together with the leader making suggestions, and then each person doing his or her own movement to that energy. Ask the group to add sounds that come out of the movement. You will find that each person's sound is as individual as their movement. Sometimes making sounds can be intimidating. You may want to find a way to gently encourage those who feel silly or uncomfortable, or tell them that making the sound is not compulsory.

At some point, when you feel it is appropriate, perhaps after 30 or 60 seconds or more, ask the group to freeze. Then choose a few people, one at a time, to make their sound and let that be the "music" for the rest of the group to move to. After each one, ask the group how this sound influenced their movement, and how it was different from their own movement and sound, even though it was the same energy. After the group has experienced the movements and sound of three to six people, ask which felt comfortable, easy, or difficult for them. Also, which of these had expanded their movement vocabulary.

Have the group choose partners and explore a conversation with their voices in a specific energy. If it is in legato, each word will be slow, even, and somewhat drawn out, without inflections or any rise or fall in volume and with no tempo changes. After a minute or so, have a short discussion about feelings and perceptions. Ask how their individual conversations went and how the energy affected what they said and what was heard.

Another related activity is to have each person do a short everyday movement in mime, such as combing hair, brushing teeth, or eating something in the same natural energy that is normally used to perform such activities. Then ask each person to practice doing the same movement in two other energies, such as swinging and percussive. Let each person perform or demonstrate their movement before the group in the three ways: normal everyday energy and the two others.

Ask each person to see how many energies they can do at one time, simultaneously. In all my years of teaching, I have only seen two people who could do all five at once and both used their eyes to do the staccato movement. This takes some coordination, even to do two or three together. It's like rubbing your stomach and patting your head at the same time. However, it is fun to try.

One more idea is to have the group pick a partner and stage a mock fight. The partners stand or sit far enough away from each other so that they do not accidentally hurt each other. First, one partner socks, hits, punches, or kicks at the other without touching, like mirror or shadowboxing. Then the other responds in movement and with sound as if they were hit. Then the one who responded reacts by punching or hitting back. Continue to take turns like a conversation. This entire process can be done in one of the energies, or the leader can have the group freeze and then change from one energy to another. This activity works very well in legato, percussive, or staccato energies.

NON-LOCOMOTOR MOVEMENTS

These are: bend, stretch, twist, swing, push, pull, dodge, strike, rock and sway, lift, sit, fall, bounce, and shake.

One at a time, explore these, first with body parts and then with whole body movements. Musical instruments can accompany the activity or appropriate music for each non-locomotor movement may be used. I have also done this activity successfully with no music. Starting with bend, the leader may suggest or ask for suggestions. Ask the group to explore how many ways each can bend, such as: bend your head front, back and side; bend your fingers; your elbows; your torso, front, side, back; your knees, etc. The group may also make their own choices for exploration.

After body part articulation ask each to make a bent body statue with their whole body at the sound of a drum or tambourine or a word signal, changing the statue and body level, when applicable, at each beat.

Statues.   Proceed with a group statue by having one person at a time go to the center and make a bent body statue, connect to one or more of the group in some way, until six to twelve people are forming a statue (see photo). Remind the group that it may be more interesting to look at if there are a variety of levels with some sitting, standing,

Figure 3-1   A Group 'BEND' Statue

kneeling, and even lying down, as well as facing various directions.

For those who can't stand or have difficulty standing, have them use their chairs or have the sitting person be the first to start the statue. This process can be repeated for each non-locomotor movement. A group statue can even combine a few different ones, such as: two people bend, three stretch and two twist.

Scripts. Members of the group can choose three or four nonlocomotor movements and do each one in succession, like a script. Or, each person can pick three or four cards from a stack of cards, each one containing a non-locomotor movement. This can be varied by doing them all legato, letting each statue pose flow into the next; or each pose can change at the beat of a drum or another signal. Transitions can be added in between each pose, such as: "Pose in *bend* turn the whole body and pose in *stretch*, walk to another place and do a *twist* pose."

Combined with Walks. Take four non-locomotor movement cards and place each one in the center facing each of the four walls so that the cards form a small square. Have the group walk or dance around the room in any way they individually wish to. Use music to motivate. The object is to touch each of the four walls with a different body part. After touching each wall each person must come to the center and do the corresponding non-locomotor movement, holding it for three counts before going to the next wall. It is important that everyone moves at their own pace.

When they have completed all four walls and all four of the non-locomotor movements, they can sit down. This is no contest and no race, just the fun of the process. In fact, you may add another element by having them say hello to each other as they pass by, or freeze in their last pose until all have finished. Or, at the beat of a drum they must touch those closest to them.

LOCOMOTOR MOVEMENTS

These include walk, run, jump, and hop. Leap is a variation of run. Skip is a combination of a step and a hop.

It is fun to throw a die and pick a card with a locomotor movement to do according to the number that comes up on the die. Another variation is to pick three or four cards and throw the die for each one. This script becomes a short phrase or the beginning of a dance.

Another variation is to have a stack of cards each containing a non-locomotor movement and a stack of cards each containing an emotion (feeling) and perhaps a third stack containing adjectives or action words. Each person would pick a card from each stack and perform, or the whole group can perform together. An example of the three cards picked might be *twist, angrily, fast.* Sometimes members of the group will come up with more ways to vary an activity creatively.

Rudolph Laban's Effort/Shape[4] is another vocabulary of movement that may be used as exploration. Laban's vocabulary was defined in this manner:

Effort

Flow:	Free	-	Bound
Weight:	Light	-	Strong
Time:	Sustained	-	Quick
Space:	Indirect	-	Direct

Combinations of effort include:

Float:	= light, slow, indirect.
Wring:	= strong, slow, indirect.
Press:	= strong, slow, direct.
Glide:	= light, slow, direct.
Dab:	= light, quick, direct.
Flick:	= light, quick, indirect.
Slash:	= strong, quick, indirect.
Punch:	= strong, quick, direct.

These can be explored in the same way as the non-locomotor movements.

Shape

Widening:	Growing	Rising	Advancing
Narrowing:	Shrinking	Sinking	Retreating
Sideward Out:	Growing	Upward	Forward
Sideward Across:	Shrinking	Downward	Backward

Laban's shape can be explored with body parts or whole body, in partners and in groups.

Chapter 4

MOVEMENT MOTIVATORS AND PROPS

A prop works as a focus outside of the self and therefore motivates movement because of the interest in the prop. I use a variety of props: some as motivators, such as scarves and bells, and some as a tool for understanding the body and how it can move, such as a skeleton. Another way in which I use props is to help initiate creativity and new ideas, as with pipe cleaners. Popping faces (see Figure 4-5) and sponge balls are wonderful motivators for squeezing the hands tight as in an isometric exercise which, if done often, can strengthen the hands and arms.

Props are fun; they add a new dimension to exercise. While using some props, one of my patients at a nursing home said, "You get the fun out of us." After my grant period, a recreation therapist who had been in the training program at the retirement home where I worked said she got a lot out of the motivational techniques I use and felt that not only had she increased the vocabulary of her movement, she had learned new methods for motivating the residents.

SCARVES

Use flowing musical accompaniment, such as a waltz. Have each participant choose a lightweight colorful scarf and hold it by one corner. The facilitator can have the group form a circle, standing or sitting, and make the following suggestions:

Reach the scarf as high and low as you can. (Repeat each movement a few times and repeat each with other arm for those who can.)

Swinging your arm in an arc, front and up to the floor behind you, then up and forward to the floor in front of you. As you reach for the floor with your right arm, bend your right knee and torso in toward the center of the circle. As you step out away from the circle, bend again, this time reaching up and behind you, attempting to touch the floor with the scarf as you swing both in and out.

For those who can turn around with the scarf, hold your arm out and let it flow in space in front of you. Turn to the right and then the left, so you can experience both directions.

Wave the scarf from side to side, as far to either side as you can.

Circle the scarf around and behind your head two or three times in one direction and then in the other.

Make a big circle with the scarf, framing your whole body first in one direction, and then in the other.

Wave and wiggle the scarf wherever you would like, perhaps trying to get it under your leg.

Have the scarf go over your head and under your body.

Throw the scarf in the air and catch it, first with both hands; then toss it from one hand to the other.

Have a game of catch with a partner. Throw your scarf at each other at the same time so that you are catching your partner's while he or she is catching yours. With the frail, I go to each and throw my scarf to them at the same time they throw theirs to me.

Create your own scarf dance.

The leader may add more scarves to this activity at this point so that the participants can have a scarf in each hand, or even playfully dress up with some around their hands, necks, waists, or wherever they wish.

This activity can end up with each participant using the scarf as in a charade, as something other then what it is, such as a headband, a mask, an apron, a tie, etc., while the rest of the class guesses.

During the scarf activity at a nursing home, one inhibited lady, who said she considered herself clumsy, got up and danced. One man with very poor vision who was usually very hard to motivate, got carried away with the scarf and didn't want to part with it.

Two-foot strips of colorful crepe paper streamers can be used in place of scarves. These can be made into creative articles to be worn and kept by the participants, such as a bracelet, a bow for the hair, a necktie, etc.

BELLS ON ANKLES AND WRISTS

Recently I attended a festival of artisans and craftspeople who were brought to this country from India. I have always enjoyed bells, and made some in the past when working at a children's summer camp. I used little jingle bells threaded through elastic which I had sewn together. There were sets for wrists, ankles, heads, and waists. But

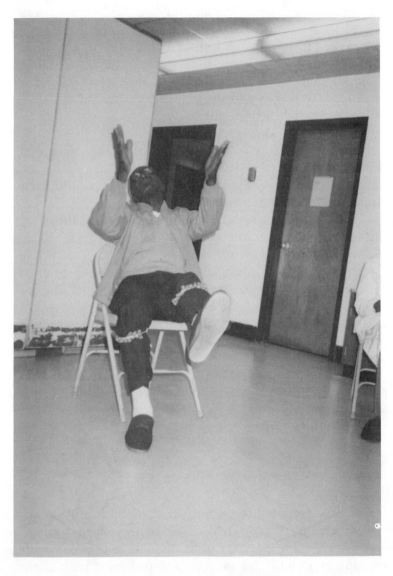

Figure 4-1   Bells on Ankles

I had never thought of using this idea with older adults. At the festival I bought a set of ankle bells and brought them into a class one day, thinking I'd use them as an instrument to shake and pass around. But when I got to class, I decided to use them as an activity, letting each person tie them around their ankles (giving help to those who needed it). Anyone wearing stockings had the choice of tying them around their wrists.

Each person had a turn dancing with them, leading the rest of us in whatever movement they felt like, or whatever movement the bells stimulated. Each person had the opportunity to dance by themselves for a while before the rest of us joined in—it was their chance to solo. Those who could not stand moved their feet, legs, and arms in their chairs.

I now find this a wonderful motivator for all populations, including the very frail. Even those who rarely stand, do so. The bells can be used on the arms as well, which motivates greater arm movements. I use African or Caribbean drum music to accompany the dancing. The sound of the bells as one moves promotes additional excitement and therefore more movement. Even those with diminished hearing are able to feel the vibrations of the bells.

ELASTIC

I have Chinese jump ropes (see Figure 4-2) that I use as initiators for creative movement. Each person explores what they can do, placing their feet on one end and their hands around the other end, stretching, twisting, and bending the arms, legs, and torso. After the class has the chance to find a variety of positions, poses, and movements with the elastic, each member can find a shape to share that everyone can mirror, giving everyone the opportunity

Figure 4-2   Elastic

to lead in turn. This can be done in a sitting and standing position.

A variation of this would be for the group to find a partner and tie their ropes together, exploring the shapes they can make together.

Skeleton

I also have a 12-inch plastic skeleton that I bought in a toy store. It was inexpensive and pops together easily. Once in a while I bring the skeleton to class and pass it around so that we can see the parts of the body I often mention. I ask everyone to look at, and try to move, the joints that bend, the rib cage, the pelvis, hip sockets, the vertebrae, and spine.

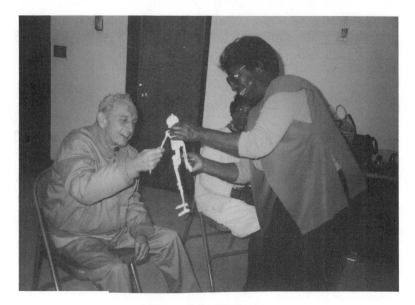

Figure 4-3   Skeleton

I never pretend to be presenting an anatomy lesson, but the more we know about ourselves, the easier it is to understand how to take care of ourselves and, the more knowledge we have about our bodies, the easier it is to take responsibility for ourselves. I find that bringing in the skeleton not only gives information, but is fun as well. Many jokes emerge.

After seeing and feeling the skeleton, it is easier to feel those parts on ourselves as we move. Sometimes we partner-up and take turns running our fingers down our partner's spine, feeling the vertebrae.

When we next do rolling down, or up, the spine and I say "vertebra by vertebra," it is more clearly understood. The experience of the skeleton can be repeated periodically, especially when presenting hands-on activities (see Chapter 9).

Pictures of a skeleton also may be used. I found that even the very frail are able to better articulate their movements after experiencing the model skeleton.

Puppets

Sometimes I bring my puppets to class and give each person the opportunity to choose one. Then I ask them to introduce themselves to their puppets. I ask them to get to know their puppets, to have a conversation with their puppet and to listen closely to what their puppet says to them. This activity has worked particularly well with the frail elderly.

The following are some of the statements that were

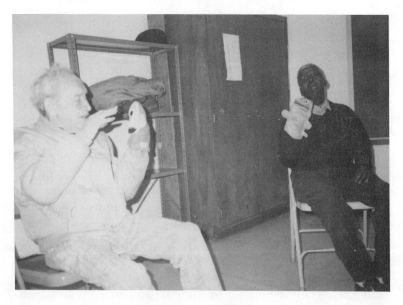

Figure 4-4   Puppets

made by puppets: "You're not very good-looking, but you're good, and when I ask you to do something you do it from your heart." "When you get ready he'll do anything." "Good morning, everybody, and I love everybody." "You can do it if you try."

In one case, a woman in the geriatric unit of a hospital wouldn't take her medication, but when the puppet asked her to, she did.

I also have had groups partner-up and have their puppets introduce each other and say something about how they felt. There are some who feel silly and uncomfortable with puppets, and they may participate by watching.

Body parts can be puppets also. For instance, an elbow can be one person's puppet while someone else's shoulder acts as a puppet. In this case, the person whose elbow is the puppet would speak the words as if the elbow were talking and the person whose shoulder was the puppet would answer as if the shoulder were responding to the other person's elbow puppet. In other words, the specific body part chosen becomes the puppet.

BIRD, POPPING FACE, AND SOFT SPONGE BALLS

I often browse through toy stores; it is surprising how much can be found that can be used to help motivate movement. The bird (see Figure 4-5) works to articulate gross motor movement in arm and shoulder. Popping faces (see Figure 4-6) are fun to watch and never fail to bring a smile to the person squeezing them, as well as to the rest of the group. As the popping faces are squeezed, the eyes, nose, and tongue pop out. These and soft sponge balls are good to help strengthen hands and lower arms when the person squeezes them. I encourage the older adults to squeeze hard and to do many repetitions.

Figure 4-5   The Bird

Figure 4-6   Popping Faces

PIPE CLEANERS

Colorful pipe cleaners also are good motivators. They are something that can be worked with outside of the body that helps to initiate bending and twisting shapes. After everyone has chosen a color, I ask that each person explore how many ways they can find to bend their pipe cleaner, making a final shape to share with the group.

Each person has the opportunity to hold up their shape and the rest of the group has the chance to move their bodies, or a body part, into as close an approximation as they can to each shape. In each group there are always interesting variations of shapes, ranging from abstract shapes to naturalistic shapes such as a flower, an animal, or an object, like an umbrella.

This activity also can be repeated to explore twisting shapes.

Figure 4-7   Pipe Cleaner Shapes

BEANBAG

The beanbag I have looks like a mole, has whiskers, is yellow with lovely eyes, a cute face, and is named Puggle. I use the beanbag to help with body part articulation, balance, and to have fun in the process. Here are some ways in which I instruct those in class to use the beanbag.

"Place the beanbag on one shoulder at a time, balancing it first and then lifting the shoulder up three times.

"While sitting in your chair, place the beanbag on each thigh, balancing it, and then lifting the knee as high as you can three or more times, keeping the beanbag from falling.

"Now balance it on your foot and lift the foot off the floor as high as you can without dropping the beanbag. Do this a few times with each foot.

"Balance the beanbag on a body part (i.e., head, elbow

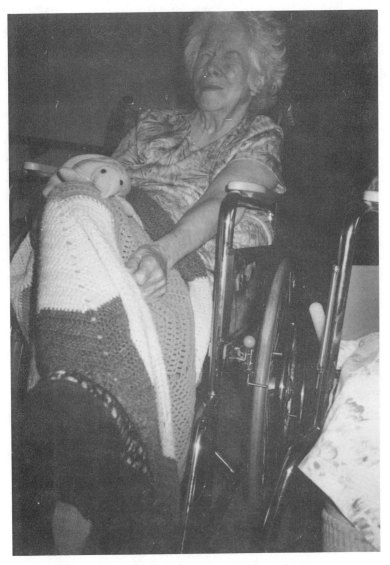

Figures 4-8   Balancing and Lifting Beanbag on Thigh

held horizontally, or a hand, palm up or down) and walk around the room."

I have had very creative variations from members of my classes. One person placed Puggle on her back after she got down on her hands and knees. Another put the beanbag in her skirt pocket, while another placed it on his foot.

"Toss the beanbag up in the air three times and catch it with both hands, and then toss it from one hand to the other. Try throwing and catching it with the same hand also." This is good for hand/eye coordination.

"In a circle, have a catch with the person on your right, throwing the beanbag to the next person after a few catches.

"Make a group circle standing, call someone's name, and throw the beanbag to that person." (This reinforces names and hand/eye coordination.)

In a circle, quickly throw the beanbag to someone who then has to do a body movement that everyone must follow. Then the beanbag is thrown to another person who does another body movement that the class follows, and so on until all have had a turn.

Still in a circle, throw the beanbag to anyone of your choice. After each person catches the beanbag, everyone must bend down and touch the floor.

WORRY DOLLS

These are tiny dolls that come in a small box and are from Guatemala. The local tradition is to take a doll from the box and give all your worries to this doll. I have brought these dolls into all of my classes and have found that everyone is able to silently give over their worries, after which there is a sense of release. The mood of the class is uplifted, we have shared in a ritual. This is done with lightness and fun, yet it is effective.

Chapter 5

AWAKENING AWARENESS

Most of us walk around with our senses and perceptions dulled. Some of us have purposely shielded ourselves from the sights and sounds we prefer not seeing and hearing and have gotten into habits of being single-focused and tunnel-visioned.

Our awareness can be stretched and expanded at any age. Once we are nudged awake and given reminders and tools to open our perceptions, it is as if a window has been opened and we can see and hear outside of the little rooms that are ourselves, into the environment around us.

PERCEPTION EXPANDERS

Here are five ideas to help expand perception.

Have everyone look around the room for one minute. Then, tell them to close their eyes and ask questions such as, "What color is the floor? What color is the ceiling? Are there pictures on the walls? Can you describe the walls and what's on them? Are there windows? What kind? Describe the window coverings and the furniture. What is the person on your right wearing? What am I wearing?"

You also could be more general and ask, "What did you see? Describe what you saw."

When possible have the group take a short walk somewhere in the building, or close by, outside. Discuss everyone's observations when you return.

Have the participants face a partner and observe him or her, taking note of as much as they can for a few minutes. Then tell them: "Turn your chairs away from each other and change three to ten things on yourself (for instance, remove some jewelry, or change a ring or bracelet from one hand to another, take off one shoe, roll up a sleeve, change your hair)." After a given amount of time have them turn back to their partners and see how many changed items they can detect.

Change something about the room you are in with each session and see who notices, or how long it takes for someone to notice.

Wear something noticeably different once in a while and see if anyone notices.

The following will not be appropriate for the very frail, confused, or visually impaired.

Draw a Path

Have each person draw a very simple shape, such as a letter of the alphabet or a simple geometric shape. Then have everyone, one at a time, either walk out the shape in a path on the floor or draw the shape in the air with a body part. Have them repeat this twice and ask them to say when they are beginning and when they are done. Next, on another piece of paper, have everyone else draw the shape they have perceived, and then share the shapes to see how many variations there are.

Variation

After everyone has demonstrated their shapes, choose three or four people to show their shapes at the same time, each starting from a different area of the cleared space. Try to choose a mixture of shapes that includes curved lines, straight lines, and perhaps zigzag lines, as seen in a triangle, the letter S, and the letter M.

This can be developed into a dance by changing the walks to runs and skips and changing their level and direction.

Add music or rhythmic accompaniment and repetitions of each person's moving shape. It is fun to choose a partner for each person and have that partner accompany the moving person with a sound or musical instrument.

SENSES

Information comes to us through our senses. The keener our awareness and perception, the greater our learning skills. The more conscious we are of our senses, the easier it is to make the connection to our cognitive selves.

As we mature the senses often diminish. Therefore, using our senses more frequently with a conscious focus on each sense is important. Enhancing observational skills is significant for anyone and particularly for people with special needs. We often are so concerned with their handicaps, we may forget about something as basic as awareness of senses. Exploring each sense fully gives the opportunity for a richer experience of life.

In one training session I led, an occupational therapist commented that sensory stimulation is useful for brain-damaged and neurological patients and said she would use the methods I had presented.

"Don't forget to stop and smell the roses" is a cliché we often hear. As Brian Way, British expert on creative dramatics, once noted, "Just think what would happen if we didn't comb our hair, brush our teeth, or bathe for three days? Yet how many of us spend just five minutes a day focusing on our senses"—to really stop and *see* as we look, to explore with our eyes in detail; to stop and hear as we listen—tuning in to *all* the sounds. How often do we actually *feel* what we touch and allow ourselves the pleasure of examining and perhaps seeing with our hands and fingers; to slow down and taste what we eat and to remember to smell the flowers as well as the scents of all things as we move through our day.

It's true that we have often put up screens to protect ourselves from the unpleasant and the bombardment of our senses; but along the way many have deadened our senses so that we have lost an important part of the sense of self.

Touch

One of the methods I use to enhance the sense of touch is to explore textures such as feathers, sandpaper, sticky tape, rubber bands, and cold cream.

Before presenting these textures I ask everyone to touch and notice the feel of their clothes, shoes, skin, hair, fingernails, the chair they are sitting in, the floor and, when possible to walk around the room, to notice the feel of things in and around the room. While they are experiencing by touching, I ask them to think about whether what they are touching is rough, smooth, bumpy, cold, warm, sticky, silky, etc.

A short discussion follows this initial touch experience. Often there are people who are surprised by the feel of things they see every day but don't normally pay attention

Figure 5-1   Feathers

to when they touch them. Then we proceed with the chosen list of textures, one at a time. After exploring each, we discuss the qualities of each, and what each is like. I ask, "What does it feel like?" Some of the responses are: "A feather is soft, light, tickly"; "It floats and twirls when you blow on it." I then ask them to tell what else is like this, or what it reminds them of. Some responses to the feather are: "It is like snow"—"birds," "a pillow," "a leaf," etc. This discussion is followed by movement, first with a body part and then the whole body, that represents the quality and properties of each texture. Suitable music is chosen for each texture to help motivate movement. This activity allows the participants to have fun while moving and thinking.

With some groups it is difficult to get responses so the leader may need to make some of the following suggestions for words describing the qualities and properties of:

Sandpaper is rough, sandy, jerky, tough, and it is like a stubble beard, toast, cement, an emery board, or a nail file.

Rubber Bands are smooth, rubbery, they can shake like Jell-O, stretch like elastic or chewing gum, slowly and quickly; wiggle like a worm, snap across the room and make shapes.

Sticky Tape is sticky like adhesive, Band-Aids, glue, paste, Velcro, and taffy. Movement would be quick and jerky, or stuck like a strong magnet.

Cold Cream is smooth, cool, creamy, slimy, sensual, silky, and slippery. It is like body oils, butter, and mayonnaise. Movement might be slithering, sliding, and melting.

During a period when I worked at a recreation center, there was a newly blind woman who responded minimally to most of what I did; but when we worked with textures she became totally involved. After each texture I collected the objects. She did not want to relinquish her sandpaper and I told her that if she was to keep the sandpaper, she'd have to have a feather in her other pocket for balance and that they were a gift for her. After that incident she took part in everything we did.

I have found that the textures awaken and motivate some people in ways that nothing else does. In one nursing home, some patients came alive and moved when they previously had been morose and very inward-looking.

Slowing down, sensing the object you are feeling can be a spiritual experience. Truly sensing is being totally with, perhaps becoming one with, that which we are sensing.

Textures can be collected on a nature walk, or brought in from home. If one texture is presented at each session, it may be possible to include drawings that depict the quality of the texture or the texture itself. The participants also can express their feelings and memories about the texture in a word or sentence that could develop into a poem or story.

Hearing and Listening Tools

Tell the group: "Close your eyes and listen to the sounds around you, inside and outside. Be quiet for a minute or two and then share what you heard with the group."

Play a piece of music and let everyone share the images that come to their minds after a few minutes.

Drawing also can be added to each of the above activities.

Sense of Smell/Scent Enhancers

Bring in envelopes and blotters with various scents in/on them (i.e., cinnamon, oregano, mint, teas, coffee, pepper, etc., in envelopes and ammonia, rose oil, coconut oil, etc., on blotters.)

Discuss memories of some of the scents and add category dances, poems, drawings, and music or sound effects.

Taste

Look for and cut out pictures of foods and discuss the taste of each as well as some of the memories connected with them. You also can bring in various foods and have a taste test, while blindfolded, either guessing the food or describing the taste of each food.

A Multisensory Process with Peanuts

In this activity the group explores a peanut with each of the five senses.

First, each participant takes a peanut in the shell from a bag that is passed around. Examining the peanut visually and carefully for a few minutes will acquaint each person with the specific aspects of their "personal" peanut. The group then can be paired off and each couple put their peanuts together—mixing them up to see if they can find their own.

This process is repeated with three or four people in a group and then with larger numbers. Individuals are able to find their own peanut with no difficulty most of the time.

The second part of this process has the participants each examine their personal peanut with their eyes closed, touching and feeling each crevice, crack, and bump of the peanut. Then, the above process of pairing off into couples, followed by trios and then larger groups, is repeated, with everyone closing their eyes and finding their own peanuts by the sense of touch.

Next, with eyes opened, have the participants smell the peanut while it is still in its shell. Then ask them to place it next to their ears and crack it open. The sound of the cracking shell is magnified and is very different when it is right next to the ear. Of course, this may not work for those with diminished hearing or a hearing impairment.

Continue to explore slowly the inside of the shell and the peanut by touch and smell. The inner shell is very smooth and silky and the scent becomes stronger. Tell them to notice the color and feel of the peanut skin and listen to it as they remove it very slowly, perhaps smelling it and then tasting it. The skin may seem papery and bitter. Before actually placing the peanut itself in their mouths, have them feel its smoothness. Tell them to part it in half, seeing the little knob inside at the top, and don't forget to have them smell it again. Before the tasting part of this activity, ask if there are any dietary restrictions or dental problems with peanuts.

When they place the peanut in their mouths, they may want to roll it around the tongue, above and under, feeling it against the inside of the cheeks and the roof of the mouth as well as the gums. When they do bite into it, ask them to do so very slowly, feeling and tasting the juice.

Tell them: "Continue to bite into the peanut so slowly that you can feel the changing texture from peanut to peanut butter, crunchy to smooth, as well as the stronger taste of peanut."

I suggest that you hold a discussion with the group about the stronger awareness of each of the senses stimulated by this process before proceeding to the next activity.

Imagery

Tell the group: "Close your eyes and imagine yourself as a peanut inside a shell. What does it smell like? What does it feel like being this size and shape? Is it dark or light? Do you feel safe, confined, or neither? What can you hear? How do you move?"

For those in chairs, the following activity can be done with a single body part. Those who can stand may want to hold onto the backs of their chairs, and those who are able can get down on the floor.

Tell them: "Imagine you're in a bowl with other peanuts and move accordingly. The bowl is being passed around and shaken. The bowl is emptied into a pan and the peanuts roasted. Some peanuts are placed in a bowl of water and are floating. Some are poured out and roll away."

Chapter 6

MOVEMENT GAMES

Movement games add structure to exploration of body movement. Like props, they help to stimulate creativity and motivate body movement. Most of the following are done in partners or groups, which creates social interaction.

OPEN/CLOSE, WIDE/NARROW, EXPAND/CONTRACT, GROW/ SHRINK, AND UNFOLD/FOLD

These are words to help explore body parts and whole body movement. Although all are similar, each has a slightly different connotation and the use of the body and muscles will change with each set of words.

Explore the eyes, mouth, hands, arms, chest, and legs one at a time, and for those who are able, the whole body, which can be done on different levels and in different directions (i.e., up, down, side, etc.).

Each of the following sets of words may initiate a different kind of feeling as well as a different way of moving

Figure 6-1　Wide

Figure 6-2　Narrow

for each person. Therefore, it is a good idea to try them all and then have a discussion about how the movement quality of each person differed for each set of words.

Open/Close (or pull in and pull out) has a quality of reaching out into the environment and coming back to self, an out and in feeling.

Wide/Narrow has an out and down, up and in quality. Widening includes a tendency towards squatting or bending. When narrowing, one may tend to go up on the toes to acquire a taller and thinner feeling and look; a sort of sucking in and lifting up.

Expand/Contract (or condense) may use the muscles more, such as loosening and tightening, and may also have a more conscious awareness and use from the center of the body (chest, diaphragm, and pelvis).

Grow/Shrink involves qualities that embody pulling into gravity, going in and down into the floor, or melting and then going upward and outward. These might be done more slowly.

Unfold/Fold has more of a piece-by-piece (body-part-by-body-part) feeling and quality to it.

Here are some other words that you may want to add to this list: spread, shorten, enlarge, extend, increase, decrease, swell, wane, stretch, inflate, reduce, melt, vanish, ebb, decline, diminish, shrivel, tighten, cramp, collapse, compact, wither, draw in, crumble.

After exploring each of these sets individually, the group can pair up and try them with partners facing each other and perhaps holding hands. This may be followed by small groups in circular or cluster formations.

MIRROR/TRIANGLE/DIAMOND

These movement games can be preceded by follow-the-leader, wherein each member of the group gets the chance to stand or sit in front of the group and do movements that the rest of the group follows. It is a good idea to remind the group that the person leading must move very slowly so that everyone can follow, as if they were a mirror image of the leader, trying to move at exactly the same moment the leader does.

This also can be done in a circle, but mirroring in a circle can get confusing as to which side of the body does the following. When performed in a circle, the lead can be given to the person on the right, as one leader finishes, by turning the head and perhaps extending the arm in a gesture of "*Your* turn."

Ask the person who is leading not to take a position that, when imitated by the others, will put them into a position where they will not be able to see what the leader does next, such as turning or placing the head down.

After the group has done this activity for a round or two and understands the concept, then it can be done by partners.

Everyone has the opportunity to lead, and for most this is a fun experience. However, there may be a few who feel intimidated by leading, and get stymied. A person who doesn't know what to do can pass the lead on to the next person. No one should be forced or coerced into leading. Allow this to be a pleasant experience rather than a tension-producing and fearful one.

Mirror

This can be done in a sitting or standing position. Ask everyone to find a partner. Both parties hold their hands up to their partner's, fingers up, palms facing but not touching. The facilitator can designate when one partner starts to lead and then can decide when to have the other partner take the lead. Or, the facilitator can tell the group that each person can take over the lead at any time and, as a result, each person has to be very observant and sensitive to every move and change in their partner's body. The person leading can start with the hands and arms, either at the facilitator's suggestion, or when the person leading feels ready. He or she may move another body part and add more and more of the body in slow movement as he or she feels more comfortable with moving and more "tuned in" to the partner.

The facilitator can ask the group of partners to freeze their positions after they have been moving for a few minutes. While the group is in these frozen statues, ask them to think about what they might be doing; to use their creative imagination to imagine what these two statues are in the midst of doing. Tell the group to remember their positions and to relax. Then have each couple share, first with each other and then with the group.

This activity can continue for 10 minutes, or even longer, by continuing to change the lead or changing partners completely. Changing partners may change how each person moves, since the movement responses are different with different people.

This brings us to a variation which is good for use with uneven numbers of people and offers chance to experience a wider range of movement and movement personalities.

Triangles and Diamonds

This activity is done in small groups of threes and fours. One person at a point of the triangle or diamond faces out and becomes the leader. The others face and follow the leader as she moves slowly. Start in place, but after the groups have had the chance to become comfortable with each other and with moving, they may want to venture through space. For the leader to give up the lead, he or she has to turn one way or the other, and then faces the person who becomes the new leader and is now the point of the triangle or diamond. This is the way the lead keeps changing and each leading person can move for as long or short a period as they feel inclined, unless the facilitator signals otherwise. It may be a good idea to have a rule that everyone must turn to the right all the time, or else the same two people may find themselves giving the lead back and forth continuously.

Some followers will find that there are some leaders' movements that feel easy and comfortable, some that are difficult for their bodies, others that stretch them into new ways of moving that they hadn't thought of before, and even some that they do not like at all. The group may have to be reminded beforehand not to do anything that may be outlandishly difficult for others, such as a headstand or a cartwheel. This is unlikely, but it can happen. They also should be told to do the best they can when following and not to be concerned if they cannot do a movement exactly the same as the leader.

This activity can also be frozen. Ask the group to freeze for a moment, at a point when the positions look interesting, and then ask them to look around while the rest of their bodies stay in these positions. This allows them to see the variety of movement and positions of the other groups. Then have them continue.

These can be done to slow moving, flowing music such as Kitaro's "Silk Road."[5]

PASSIVE/ACTIVE IN PARTNERS

Ask everyone to find a partner. Have one member of each couple sit in a chair and relax as much as possible, allowing the arms and legs to be limp. This person is the passive one. The active partner will first test how relaxed the other is by lifting his or her arm and asking the partner to feel like a rag doll, to pretend that the arm weighs a ton. The active partner can lift the arm and let go of it to see if it will drop down. Some people cannot relax enough to do this and their arms will remain in the air, or they will find themselves helping their partners. This can be practiced a few times. Sometimes it is just a matter of trusting another person with your body and that too takes practice and time.

There are a number of ways you can now begin the activity. Tell the active person to proceed by placing the partner's body (arms, hands, heads, legs) in a pose that will form a sculpted creation (see photo.) When everyone is finished, you can have the active group walk around the room to see all the statues. Then have everyone change partners and repeat the process.

PASSIVE/ACTIVE IN GROUPS

Divide the class in half, asking one half to be "active" and the other half to be "passive." The passive group can sit in their chairs or on the floor in the center of the room while the active group makes a statue of the passive group, connecting each person by one body part or another. A statue can be made by lifting someone's arm or leg in the passive group and having another person in the passive group hold up that arm or leg with their shoulder or head. The group should be advised to be careful how they place the body parts and to be sure the positions cause no injuries. However, anyone in the passive group can at any time become active. This causes a constantly changing statue as well as changing groups, since anyone in the active group can also decide at any time to become passive.

If you should ever find that everyone has decided to be passive, you may need to request some active participants. The opposite also may occur, in which case you will

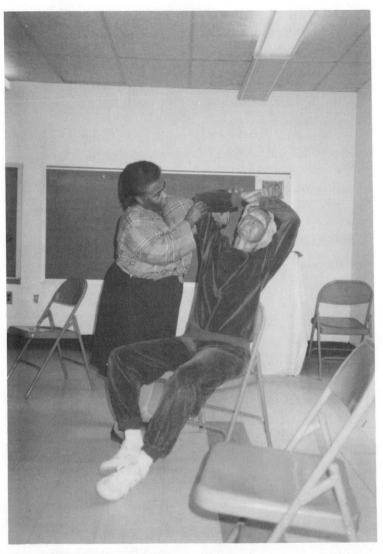

Figure 6-3 Passive/Active in Partners

need to request some passive members. You may end this movement game at any time. Quiet music such as a lullaby or Japanese koto music can be used to set the mood.

FILL-INS

Ask one person to start this movement game by making a body shape in the center of the circle. Then have the next person fill in this shape by either getting underneath the first person or in some way covering him or her by placing their body in a shape on top but without touching, so that the first person can come away. Then, one at a time, each member of the group can take a turn filling in the previous body shape with their own body until the entire class has had a turn.

In another variation the group can be divided in half. The first half can make a group shape that the second group can fill in.

A TISSUE

This movement game takes concentration, coordination, and sensitivity. Give everyone a tissue (a scarf can be used instead) and then ask them to place it in their right hand and find a partner. Tell them all to hold the other end of their partner's tissue in their left hand. Have each couple decide who will begin and, at a signal, ask them to tell their partner what they like to do best, while at the same time both are moving up and down as well as under or over the tissue and their arms, and any other way that they can move while continuing to hold onto the tissue without having it tear. However, if the tissue does tear they may take another. While this is easier to do with a scarf or a crepe paper streamer, by using a tissue, one has to take

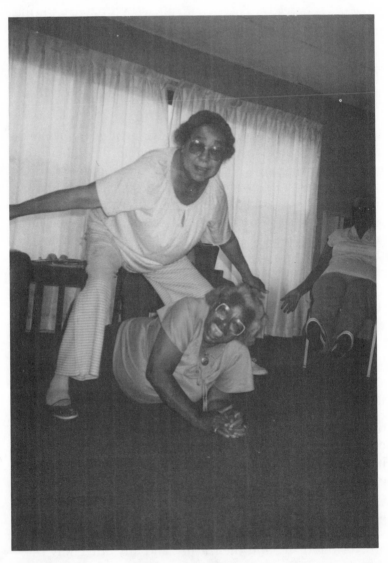

Figure 6-4   Fill-Ins

more care in moving and must pay more attention to one's partner's movement as well as to one's own.

The subject can be any category you wish, such as sharing what they did the day before, telling a story about a family member or a friend, or expressing an opinion about an issue in the news.

A variation to this movement game is to have the partners join another couple so that there are groups of four. There also can be a group of six if there is a couple left over. Again, each person takes hold of the tissue belonging to the person next to them and, while the group is moving, everyone takes turns introducing themselves, or telling what their favorite color is and why. Ask one person at a time to begin at a given signal. You may also have the group freeze at some point and then see if they can untangle without letting go of the tissue.

This can be repeated by having two groups of fours joining to make groups of eight. At this point the conversations can be transformed to passing a sound from person to person while moving up and down, over and under and all around.

As a conclusion to this game, ask everyone to make something creative with their tissue. Then have each person show their "masterpiece" and perhaps tell what it is and what it is for.

Chapter 7

MEMORY JOGGERS AND COMMUNICATION MOTIVATORS

REMEMBERING AND SHARING

For those who have not worked with many older adults it is important to become aware of and to overcome stereotyped perceptions. Many older adults themselves have been conditioned by biased and ageist negative views ingrained in our culture. I highly recommend *Truth About Aging, Guidelines for Accurate Communications,* published by the American Association of Retired Persons, 1984.

The following suggested activities often uncover rich experiences. Sometimes common experiences are discovered among group members; but even when this is not the case, the sharing always brings the group closer together because they have shared personal stories and learned more about each other. These sharings are stimulating and help the group become more socially interactive. When the buzz-buzz of verbal interaction occurs, thereby increasing the energy level, it is easier to get people moving and there is more physical interaction.

When sharing, the participants become more animated and excited, which in itself is physical action. Comparisons between past and present can be made to feed the conversations. Sometimes a group sharing develops out of my sharing something that has happened to me.

My favorite story to share is what happened on a recent birthday. I was having my annual celebration party. Rusty, one of my three sons, arrived from out of town the evening before with two of his friends whom I know well, since they had all grown up together. They brought an enormous box into my apartment and said it was a surprise present that I couldn't open until right before the party. They warned me that I wasn't to go near it, touch it, or smell it.

All the next day we decorated the apartment and prepared food for the party. Just before I went to get dressed, my younger son, Kevin, called from out of town to wish me a happy birthday and to tell me that he was sorry he couldn't be with me but was there in spirit. Feeling touched and happy I went to get dressed. When I came back into the living area I was told by Rusty I could now open my gift. I slowly began opening the box when all of a sudden out jumped my younger son. It was the biggest surprise I had ever received in my life. I was both surprised and shocked, so shocked that my mind was in a state of confusion. I could not compute; my thoughts ran on: "Was he in the box all night?" "How did he call me from the box?" As it turned out, he had just come in by train, called me from one block away, and had been sneaked into the apartment and into the box while I dressed. After sharing this story I ask for other surprise stories.

Other categories I use are: your memory of your earliest birthday, or your favorite birthday, your first day at school, your memory of your earliest Christmas or your favorite Christmas or other special holiday, memory of your first boyfriend/girlfriend (sweetheart), things you have done with your hands, legs, body, or your life, and what you remember most about the town where you grew up. When asking this last question I ask each person to say in what city, state, and country he grew up.

When asked if she remembered her first boyfriend, one woman answered, "Remember him? I married him!"

Some things we at Cole Senior Center have done with our hands:

"Hoed and picked cotton."

"Drew water out of the well."

"Made white lightning. Had a still and used the corn whiskey for medicinal purposes."

"Culled hops. I would place it in a jar and put rock candy in it, let it soak and it would get syrupy. When diluted it would break up asthma spells for children."

On special holidays, such as Thanksgiving, Mother's Day and, depending upon the ethnic background of the group, Passover or Martin Luther King Day, I have discussions about past experiences with these holidays and ask how each plans to celebrate the holiday this year. I have heard some wonderful stories. For example, on one Martin Luther King Day, Helen Maul, a black woman from the Cole Senior Center recalled the 1968 riots in D.C. when all the schools and government buildings were closed and all the government workers were being excused. "It was the first time in my 20 years of work at the Commerce Department building that I had seen the iron doors shut. While we were waiting for our husbands to come pick us up, one white woman was hysterical because her husband had called to say he couldn't get across the bridge into D.C. She asked several people if she could get a ride to the Southeast where her husband could pick her up. We had heard that several white persons had been injured with rocks thrown by angry young blacks into their cars. One man and his wife agreed to take her if she was willing to lie on the floor in the back. On our way home my husband and I ran into a detour where rioting was going on. We had to go out to the Maryland line. Young blacks lined the streets and stoned all cars with whites in them, breaking windshields and windows. Cars with blacks were told to go through. Maryland state troopers with machine guns were daring the young blacks to come over the line with their rocks."

I also use songs as topics for discussion and dance. I play "Grandma's Hands"[6] by Bill Withers and then ask each person for a hand movement that we then put into a hand dance to the song. Or I ask what each person remembers about their grandmother or grandfather. One woman got teary eyed reminiscing how she loved to take walks with her grandfather. In sharing that story she was also sharing her feelings.

Another song I play is "My Favorite Things" from *The Sound of Music*. Then each person shares a favorite thing of theirs, which we make into a mime dance.

"Lay Your Burden Down" is a spiritual and, while playing it to a group, we metaphorically find ways to place each of our own burdens down, finding different ways to place things of different sizes and weight down on the floor. After this song I like to ask everyone to say what they are thankful for. This is also a question I ask at Thanksgiving time. There are a wonderful variety of responses, ranging from the humorous to the very basic, such as food and shelter.

"Best You Can Do"[7] and "You're A Friend of Mine"[8] by Bill Withers are both upbeat songs. I ask people to dance to them in their own way. Then I ask them to go in to the center, one at a time, so everyone can follow and do the center person's dance with them. After everyone has had a turn in the center, we all go back to doing our own dance. With the very frail I go to each person, hold their hands, and dance with them. I ask the rest to keep the beat by clapping and dancing with as many body parts as they like.

"When The Saints Go Marching In" is a great picker-upper. You can make up words about moving the body and body parts.

> When the saints go marching in
> When the saints go marching in
> Oh, I want to be in that number
> When the saints go marching in
>
> (Repeat refrain)
>
> (Clap your hands)
> When we all clap our hands
> When we all clap our hands
> Oh, I want to be in that number
> When we all clap our hands
>
> (Stamp your feet)
> When we all stamp our feet
> When we all stamp our feet
> Oh, I want to be in that number
> When we all stamp our feet.[9]

You can add any body movement you would like and then ask a few people, "You tell me," and have them add another body movement. You and members of your class can make up your own movement songs to any rhythm, such as:

Put your hands up to the ceiling,
Stamp your feet and clap your hands.

Old children's songs are often fun and are appreciated by older adults such as the "Hokey Pokey." Many old dances, such as the "Bunny Hop" and "Alley Cat" are also fun to do.

Any of the above communication initiators can be developed into an activity involving other arts. Each person can do a drawing depicting the subject, or a group mural project can be developed. Mime and movement can be created and either put to music or developed into a drama. Old photographs of grandparents or hometowns can be brought in to be made into a collage. New photos can be taken for pictures of "My Favorite Things" or the "What I Am Thankful For" activity.

Say Something Nice to Each Person in the Group

Have each person in the group sit in the center of the circle and slowly turn as each person on the outside of the circle expresses something they like or feel about the person in the center. Typical comments are: "I like the way you always have a smile for everyone," "The bright colors you wear cheer me up," "I admire your flexibility," or "I'm glad you are a part of this group." Be sure to remind everyone to be sincere, to find something to say that will be honest even if it is to say, "I don't know you well enough yet to know what I like about you." If that is the case, then you can suggest that they pair up the next time there is an activity that requires partners.

Homework Reminders

As part of each session I often like to give the class what I call a "thought reminder." I tell them this is their homework for the week or until I see them next. The next time we meet I might ask for feedback: "Who remembered, and what happened?"

Examples of some thought reminders:

Watch Your Thinking

We often bring ourselves down or keep ourselves in a depressed state by focusing on negative thoughts. Be aware of how often you say "Isn't it awful?" or "terrible," or "sad." It's true life has awful, terrible, and sad events, but there are also beautiful, joyous, and uplifting events. I believe it is important to focus on the positive rather than the negative. Practice saying, "Isn't it beautiful?"—"Isn't it wonderful?" and "Isn't it magic?" And look for those aspects in life.

Be Good to Yourself

"Give yourself permission to do something good for yourself every day. Make the time to rest if you need to; cook yourself something special; visit with a friend; call someone who's on your mind."

Find Things to Laugh About

Humor is so important. Don't forget to be able to laugh at yourself. This is a good reminder for me when I get bogged down or become too intense. You might even ask everyone to bring in a funny story to share; something that happened to them or something they heard or read about.

Be Extra Considerate

When I give this assignment, , most people say, "I *am* considerate!" I tell them to take one day and be extra conscientious about everyone they come in contact with, to extend themselves beyond the norm.

Practice Eye Contact

"Make eye contact when you communicate with someone, even if your verbal exchange is brief, such as with the checkout counter person at the market. Try to make eye contact with as many people as you can." Have a practice session in the class. "Say hello to more people, even strangers. You will be amazed how many smiles you collect when you notice and acknowledge someone."

Thought for the Day

I often bring in a quote from a book, or something for contemplation. These can come from anywhere—poetry, spiritual material, or even something someone you know said. Whenever I come across a good reminder, I file it away. I now have a collection of quotes, thoughts, sayings, and affirmations.

After sharing one of these, I might ask if anyone has any comment or response.

Here are some that I use:

The only gift is a portion of thyself. . .
                              —Ralph Waldo Emerson

I believe in the sun even when it is not shining
I believe in love even when I feel it not,
I believe in God even when He is silent.
                    —Sign on a concentration camp wall

Beach Story

A woman noticed that when her life was going well for her and she took her usual walk on the beach, there were two sets of footprints. But when she was depressed or things were hard for her there was only *one* set of prints.

During a bad depression she spoke to the Lord and asked, "Why is it when I *really* need you, you're not there?"

And the Lord answered, "Dearest, the times you have seen only one set of prints are the times I have carried you!"

—Unknown

The following is a letter written by Benjamin Franklin to Miss Hubbard on the occasion of the death of his brother, John Franklin:

Philadelphia, 23rd Feb., 1756. I condole with you. We have lost a most dear and valuable relation. But it is the will of God and nature that these mortal bodies be laid aside when the soul is to enter into real life. This is rather an embryo state, a preparation for living. A man is not completely born until he be dead. Why, then, should we grieve that a new child is born among the immortals, a new member added to their happy society?

We are spirits. That bodies should be lent us while they can afford us pleasure, assist us in acquiring knowledge, or in doing good to our fellow-creatures, is a kind and benevolent act of God. When they become unfit for these purposes and afford us pain instead of pleasure, instead of an aid become an encumbrance, and answer none of the intentions for which they were given, it is equally kind and benevolent that a way is provided by which we may get rid of them. Death is that way. We ourselves, in some cases, prudently choose a partial death. A mangled, painful limb which cannot be restored we willingly cut off. He who plucks out a tooth parts with it freely, since the pain goes with it; and he who quits the whole body parts with all pains and possibilities of pains and diseases which it was liable to or capable of making him suffer.

Our friend and we were invited abroad on a party of pleasure which is to last forever. We could not all conveniently start together, and why should you and I be grieved at this, since we are soon to follow and know where to find him? Adieu, B. Franklin."

—*Strangers Among Us,* Ruth Montgomery

. . . There is no such thing as a "bad experience, but only opportunities to learn and grow in inner understanding . . . Our stumbling blocks are stepping stones.

—*Strangers Among Us,* Ruth Montgomery

. . . He who has a WHY to live can bear with almost any HOW.

—*Man's Search For Meaning,* Viktor E. Frankl

. . . everything can be taken from a man but one thing: the last of the human freedoms—to choose one's attitude in any given set of circumstances; to choose one's own way.

—*Man's Search for Meaning,* Viktor E. Frankl

. . . you do have a terminal illness: it's called death. A few years more or less time before you are washed away makes little difference. Be happy now, without reason—or you never will be at all.

. . . Act happy, feel happy, be happy, without a reason in the world. Then you can love, and do what you will.

—*Way of the Peaceful Warrior,* Dan Millman

... If you are ignorant, old age is a famine. If you are learned it is a harvest.

... One becomes what one displays.

... When people have made peace with death, they live with greater consciousness. Every day, every moment becomes more complete in itself. It makes people impatient with trivia, decorum, deception, because every moment counts, for good or ill.

—*Number Our Days,* Barbara Myerhoff

... Each one of us determines the beliefs by which he lives ... Our world is not held together by our worrying about it. We can lead a life that is free of fear. Just as I am, you are the determiner of everything that happens to you.

"An attitude can heal ... simply think what it pleases you to think, what rests and comforts you ... simply take careful notice of what makes you happy to think, and what makes you unhappy, and your mind will make the necessary adjustments itself ...

"... Words are irrelevant to what we teach and learn ... The EXPERIENCE of love and peace is the only thing of importance that is communicated. It is this attitude of the heart and not what is said between two people that does healing work in both directions. One party's accumulation of verbal knowledge is of little use to deep inner healing.

"... Love Is Our Essence ... The love in us can unite with the love in others, but two bodies cannot become one.

"... It is what we all do with our hearts that affects others most deeply. It is not the movements of our body or the words within our mind that transmit love. We love from heart to heart.

"... A good rule for mental conduct is: think whatever makes you truly happy to think.

". . . The mind can always be put to love rather than to one more review of what is already finished. Let bygones be bygones: let love be now.

". . . there is nothing in the material world as important as the love of God in our hearts. To allow a gradual and ever increasing release of that love is our only function."

—*Teach Only Love*, Gerald G. Jampolsky, M.D.

"What is real," asked the Rabbit one day when they were lying side by side, "does it mean having things that buzz inside you and a stick-out handle?" "Real isn't how you're made," said the Skin Horse, "it's a thing that happens to you when a child loves you for a long time, not just to play with but Really loves you, then you become Real." "Does it hurt?" asked the Rabbit. "Sometimes," said the Skin Horse, for he was always truthful. "When you are Real you don't mind being hurt." "Does it happen all at once, like being wound up, or bit by bit?" "It doesn't happen all at once. You become. It takes a long time. That's why it doesn't often happen to people who break easily, or have sharp edges or have to be carefully kept. Generally, by the time you are Real, most of your hair has been loved off and your eyes drop out and you get loose at the joints and very shaky. But these things don't matter at all because once you are Real you can't be ugly, except to people who don't understand."

—*The Velveteen Rabbit*, Margery Williams

Sometimes I just give the quote in our closing circle, and say it's the thought for the day, without any further discussion.

Chapter 8

POEMS AND DRAWINGS

Because my background and training are in dance, and my focus starts with the body, when I do an activity that involves other art forms, I usually start with movement. There are other times, however, when I might begin with either music, art, or poetry.

I find that older adults enjoy the creative processes. Many have never had the opportunity to explore their creativity in the arts. A few may feel silly or intimidated at times, but most often, once they start, they do get involved.

Armin Grams has pointed out in his article, "Overcoming Barriers to Creativity In Old Age"[10] that a study of a group of 70-year-olds at the University of California showed that, as the subjects grew older, they demonstrated increasing diversity and uniqueness.[11]

Staying in touch with the child within us is important throughout life. Mencius, who lived in China in the fourth century B.C., said: "A great person is one who never loses the heart of a child."

In the article "Creative Arts: A Threshold To Renewed Life," Ronald Manheimer says, "There is a magical, sometimes fearful, sensation to creativity because one is, in a sense, reinventing the world. While there is a strong element of play, it is play accompanied by a deep seriousness and sense of risk. Creative experiences expand the person's perceptions . . . Creativity . . . can empower a person to take greater initiative in all areas of life and to find bonds of solidarity with peers.[12]

Before I start a creative process I sometimes talk about how we see things, our varied perspectives, how difficult communication can be, and how the arts can be a means for communication.

HAIKU

I use the concept of the haiku as a means for an integrated arts project, focusing on communication and interpretation. I begin with a Sufi story about communication and expectation.

> A man receives a letter saying he will receive a gift of a chair in the mail. In his mind he envisions a carved wood, tufted velvet, thronelike chair and gets very excited. He can hardly wait for the chair to arrive and when it finally does he finds it is a folding metal chair.

Now, given that we all speak the same language, we assume that a simple everyday word like "chair" can easily be understood. I ask each person to close their eyes and see the first chair that comes to their mind and then ask each to describe their chair and maybe share a story about the chair if it was one that had personal meaning to them. Examples included: "one that was in my home as I grew up"; "one my dad always sat in"; "one I fed, or nursed, my children in," etc. I ask for each to describe the chair in detail (i.e., what kind of wood, metal, fabric, color, or other material). In other words, "Be as specific as you can." Often there are only two chairs that are alike or similar in a group of 20 or 30 people.

A discussion follows about our different perceptions from our diverse backgrounds and how communication is not easy—how misunderstanding or misinterpretation can evolve.

I then read a few haikus, one at a time, and ask the group to close their eyes, listen, and allow their minds to picture images. Then I ask them to share their images for each poem. Realization of our diverse perceptions is discussed, reminding us that *all* are correct; there are no "right" answers. What we perceive is our reality.

Depending upon the ability of the group, I may read the rules of writing a haiku: The poem consists of three lines; first line, five syllables; second line, seven syllables; and, third line, five syllables. In a haiku there is usually a name of a season, or a key word to imply it, a reference to nature, and a feeling. There is implied identity between two different things.

But most often I will choose a category, such as, "A Rainy Day," "Chairs," "Summertime," and ask for words and sentences expressing ideas, feelings, and memories about this chosen category. I say, "Tell me what comes to your mind when you think of summertime." Each person can write their own poem, or I write the words and sentences down as they are spoken, sometimes rearranging them, or repeating one word a few times when I read it back.

After I read the entire poem, I ask everyone to do a drawing that will express their feelings and opinions about the poem. This can be done individually or as a group mural.

The next part of this process is to add sound effects

and music. The sound effects can be a hissing sound done by the whole group to represent the wind, or by rattling paper to sound like leaves, or bells to represent birds, or a rhythmic clapping of hands as a background. Music can be made using musical instruments or a tape of one or more pieces of music.

When each person has done their own poem, you can have small groups of three or four make stanzas and each group can create their own dance, drawing and accompaniment. But when the group has made the poem together, they also can create the dance together, with or without the help of the teacher.

The following are some sample poems from some of my classes:

THE MOON

The sky
I think of light
I wonder if it's a blue moon or an orange moon?
Is it true that there's a man in the moon?
Or does it just appear to be?
Full Moon
Silver Moon
Harvest Moon
Hot Moon
The population increases on the full moon
Bride soon
Honeymoon too
Half Moon! Quarter Moon and Crescent Moon too.
                                        —Cole Center, August '85

SUMMER TIME

Flowers blooming
Moonlight
The warm sun and breezes

Swimming and biking and boating
Bar-B-Q-ing and Picnics
                    —Hill Haven Nursing Home, August '85

MY FAVORITE THINGS

Playing records to my poetry
Buying clothes
Buying clothes
Cooking
Watching TV
Shopping for holly at the five and ten cent store
Shopping for skirts at Marianne
Eating ice cream
Buying clothes
Listen to the FM station day
Shopping for groceries, especially fruit at the
    Safeway or Giant.
—Greater Southeast Community Center for the
    Aging Saturday Program for deinstitutionalized
        mentally ill clients from St. Elizabeth's Hospital.

ELDER HOSTEL

No, not so elder
And certainly not hostel
Help, please call Boston.
—Evelyn Griffith, Midland Park, N.J. Elder Hostel
    at Columbia Union College, D.C.
                    (This is an example of a Haiku)

THREE-PART DRAWINGS

At the very beginning of a session, ask everyone to
draw their mood. Using crayons and Magic Markers, tell
the class that they may draw anything in any way they want

to, from abstract to realistic. Do a second drawing after a movement sequence or activity, and a third drawing after a relaxation. Compare and discuss the drawings at the end of the class. Ask each person in the circle to place their drawings in front of them, facing the outside of the circle, with the first drawing on the left, the second drawing in the middle, and the third drawing on the right. When comparing the differences from the first to the third, look for change in colors, how the space is used, change from realistic to more abstract style, increase in energy in the drawing, and energy transformed to a center. They usually can see a calm, quiet quality in their drawings after the relaxation, for example.

INTERPRETING COLORS

Have a discussion about what a specific color means to each person in the group, and how this color makes them feel. You might start with *red* and display a few red items, such as a scarf, red crayons, and red construction paper. Bring in red objects, such as red pipe cleaners, buttons, tissue paper, and colored pictures from magazines.

After discussing feelings about this color, ask for movement that might express the color, and put this movement into a dance. You also may want to ask the participants to do a drawing or collage all in one color, individually, or as a group.

DRAW AND MOVE

Another way to initiate a multi-arts process is to start with music. Choose a dramatic piece of music and have the class close their eyes, listen, and then do a drawing

depicting the images in their imagination, or their interpretation of the music. This can be followed by writing a
poem about the music.

You also could start with a piece of art work and let
the group write a poem about what they see, followed by
choreographing a dance to express the painting.

INTERPRET MUSIC WITH DRAWING AND DANCE

Begin this by having each person lead a recording of
an orchestra with a stick or a crayon as a baton, playing a
chosen piece of music, such as a waltz. Suggest that the
rest of the group follow the person conducting with a body
part (e.g., lead the orchestra with your head, finger, or
elbow). A scarf can be tied to the stick to give the movement
more flow, or a bannerlike quality.

This can be followed by giving everyone paper and
crayons and asking them to allow the movement of conducting to flow onto the paper, using as many colors as
they wish. If it is difficult to move the group to a table,
trays can be distributed and the drawings can be done on
laps.

When the music has been stopped and everyone is finished, have each member display his or her drawing, while
the whole group interprets each drawing with body part
and whole body movement, first without the music and
then with the music.

Try this with different types of music, some flowing,
like the waltz, and some staccato, such as disco. The differences in drawings and movement will range from curved
and circular lines (waltz) to sharp, jagged, and angular lines
(disco).

This also can be done as a group mural, with everyone
working at once, perhaps moving into other people's

drawings. The movement can be interpreted section by section, or they can interpret any part of the mural they wish in small groups or all together, standing or in chairs.

MURALS AND GROUP DRAWINGS

I have already mentioned that a group mural can be done to interpret the group poem. Individual drawings can be put together to make a group collage. You can start by choosing a subject, and have the group do a mural after a discussion. Or, pass one large piece of paper from person to person, having each add to it to make one mural.

STRAW DRAWINGS

These can help promote deeper breathing as well as expand the creative imagination. Dilute tempera paint with water, testing to find the right consistency that will flow smoothly, but is not too watery. Place about one tablespoon of this mixture on a piece of paper for each person. Each person takes a drinking straw and blows directly onto the paint. (Be sure to warn them not to suck in or they will inhale the paint.) The air will blow the paint into designs they can devise.

When these are finished, the process can be extended by using the imagination and creating another picture. Have everyone share their straw drawing and ask what each person sees. Remind them to allow their imaginations to go wild. Then let them add to their drawing with crayons, carrying the composition further in any way that occurs to them.

Chapter 9

RELAXATION, IMAGERY, AND TOUCH

RELAXATIONS

Many people have difficulty falling asleep. Sometimes we are anxious, in pain or frustrated, among other negative feelings that can cause stress and tension. The following are a few techniques that are easily taught and learned. It must be remembered that, although tools can be readily acquired, if they are not practiced and used they can't do any good. It is each person's responsibility to give himself permission to say "Halt, Stop," and take a few minutes to do something that will help relax. It may be easier to pop a pill, but it is healthier to let your body and mind rest and find your center by deep breathing, and by relaxing, using one of the following methods.

Play no music, or make it gentle meditative music. Environmental music, such as the ocean or a gurgling brook, also is appropriate.

Whenever possible, do these exercises sitting in an upright position, back straight, feet uncrossed and placed on the floor, hands gently resting on the lap. If you are wearing anything with a binding fit, such as a tight waistband or glasses or jewelry, loosen or remove it. Have the following instructions *slowly, softly, and gently* read by the reader; or have someone tape them.[14]

Watch Breath

"Close your eyes and concentrate on your breath. If you have difficulty keeping your eyes still while they are closed, try focusing on the bridge of your nose with your eyes closed. This helps to keep them still. Focus on the area around your nose, slowly breathing in as deeply as you can, all the way down to your toes. Then slowly breathe out as far as you can, emptying your body of breath. Breathe in fully and breathe out fully. Breathe in and fill your body with breath, following your breath all the way in and all the way out. Notice the coolness of your breath as it enters your body, following it all the way in, and notice the warmth of your breath as it exits your body. Coolness in—warmth out; coolness in—warmth out.

"Become aware of any thoughts that enter your mind, take note of them, but do not get attached to them. Let go of the thoughts as if they were puffs of smoke or clouds dissipating, or a wave in the ocean curling over and riding from the beach back out to sea.

"Bring your attention back to your breath, breathing in and breathing out. Remember that breath is the bridge to life; breathe deeply. Take note of the split second of no breath, when you change from breathing in to breathing out, and see if you can hang there a couple of seconds longer." (Reader, wait a few seconds before giving the next suggestion.) "Now repeat this in the split second when there is no breath between breathing out and breathing in." (Again, allow time before continuing.) "Repeat both of these once again."

Refrain

After each relaxation method (Watch Breath, Sets of Four, and Body Part by Part to follow) I use a reentry that helps to bring the attention of each person back to an awakened state.

"Become conscious of how your feet are making contact with the floor and how your hands are making contact with your legs. Feel the weight of your hands on your lap. Just be aware; don't think about it. Pay attention to how your body is making contact with the chair. What parts of your body are touching the chair, and how (i.e., are some parts pressing or leaning, or do you feel as if the chair is holding you up)? Take another deep breath and slowly become aware of those around you and the room you are in. And, when you are ready, open your eyes."

Ask for responses. "How do you feel? Were you able to relax?" Someone may fall asleep; that's okay. Most will be very relaxed, quieted down, and not very talkative.

Sets of Four

Tell the group: "Close your eyes and take a few *very* slow and deep breaths, being aware of breathing in as far as you can—plus a little more—and then breathing out as far as you can, plus a little more. Now slowly and deeply breathe in through your nose and out through your nose, repeating this four times. Breathe as if there is a feather in front of your nose that you don't want to blow away.

"Now slowly and deeply breathe in through your nose and out through your mouth, repeating it four times."

"Follow this with slow and deep breathing in through your mouth and out through your nose, again repeating four times."

"Finish this process with four slow and deep breaths in and out of your mouth." Follow this with refrain/reentry described earlier.

Body Part by Part[13]

(10–15 minutes.) Read very slowly, giving enough time between each instruction. This may be done in a sitting position, legs uncrossed, hands resting on the legs, body tall. Or, when possible, do it lying on your back, legs uncrossed and straight out from your hips, arms at your side. Tell the class:

"Close your eyes, take a few slow and deep breaths, then breathe naturally and, preferably, through your nose. Allow the mouth to remain slightly open so that you don't clench your teeth or jaw.

"If lying on your back, let your head roll gently from side to side to be sure there is no tension in your neck, and then bring your head back to center. Each time you inhale, focus on a body part, and each time you exhale, feel that body part relaxing, melting, and letting go.

"Starting at the top of your head, concentrate on your scalp as you inhale and as you exhale, *let go,* feeling every follicle of hair melting away. As you breathe in, pay attention to your forehead; when you exhale, *let go.*

"Now bring your attention to your eyebrows, eyelids, and eyes and as you exhale, relax, let go. Bring your consciousness to your ears and your cheeks and as you breathe out, let go. Now focus on your mouth, your teeth and gums and tongue, and when you exhale, feel them melting away.

"At the point above the bridge of your nose and at the hairline, imagine two lines following the hairline all the way around your ears and to the nape of your neck; then imagine these lines traveling around the front to your chin where they meet before entering your mouth. Now imagine this line traveling around the inside and outside of your lower and upper gums.

"Move your attention down to your neck and shoulders, and as you breathe out, let go, relax. Now let your attention travel down your arms, upper and lower, and relax. Let your mind's eye travel down to your wrists and hands and each and every finger, one at a time. Right hand: little finger . . . ring finger . . . middle finger . . . index finger and thumb. Left hand: thumb . . . index finger . . . middle finger . . . ring finger and little finger.

"Gently bring your focus to your spine, and allow your mind's eye to travel down your spine, vertebra by vertebra, all the way down to your coccyx bone, the tail end of your spine." (Reader, make sure you give sufficient time for these instructions.)

"Let your focus travel to your chest and rib cage, feeling the body let go. Place your attention next on your pelvis . . . hips . . . stomach and buttocks and, as you exhale, relax—relax. Allow your focus to travel down your legs: thighs . . . knees and lower legs . . . let go. Picture your ankles and feet—letting go of your heels, metatarsals (arches) and the balls of your feet, and one toe at a time, let go. Left foot: big toe . . . next toe . . . middle toe . . . next toe and little toe. Repeat with the right foot as well. Feel the weight of your body and the impression it is making on the chair, floor, or bed.

"Scan your body, up and down. If you find any places where there is tension, focus your mind on that spot and breathe into it, imagining the spot filling with bubbles of air or white light and, as you exhale, feel the tension float away."

Complete process with refrain/reentry.

IMAGERY

Your imagination can take you anywhere you would like to go. You can journey outward as far as you would like in time and space, or inward to the core of your being. There are no limits to what you can imagine. The following are some suggested guided imagery. For further information on this subject see books such as: *Creative Visual-*

ization by Shakti Gawain (Bantam Books, 1979), *Visualization* by Adelaide Bry (Harper & Row, 1979) *Go See the Movie in Your Head* by Joseph Shorr, and (Ross Erikson) *Getting Well Again* by O. Carl Simonton, M.D., Stephanie Matthews Simonton, and James Creighton (Bantam Books, 1978).

Before beginning, you may want to ask everyone to close their eyes and picture their living quarters. Ask them to count the windows, to see in their mind's eye a favorite painting, photo, or memento in their home. This will offer practice in imaging. Some people may need a few practice sessions before they are able to envision images.

Music as an Image Maker

Choose a piece of music without words, such as a Beethoven or Mozart selection, preferably a piece that may be unfamiliar so that there is not a preconceived image.

Have everyone close their eyes and tell them to let their minds wander freely. Ask them to see what images come to them. What pictures does the music invoke for them, what does it remind them of? Let the music play for three to five minutes, giving the group some time for their minds to conjure up visions and stories. Bring the group back by slowly turning down the sound of the music and gently asking everyone to open their eyes. Ask them one at a time to share what they saw.

Freedom Dance

Choose a piece of music without words, preferably more active, such as Paul Horn's *Inside 11*[15] or Jean Michel Jarre's *Equinoxe*.[16] Tell everyone to close their eyes and, while continuing to sit, to imagine themselves dancing wherever they want. Say, "You are able to do anything you want, there are no limitations, you can see yourself dancing on a beach, in a meadow, or in a large ballroom—in fact, anywhere, since it is your choice; let yourself go."

Let the music play for about five minutes and then slowly turn down the sound and ask everyone to open their eyes. Start the music over from the beginning and ask everyone to stand up and dance as they did in their mind's eye. Those who can't stand or who are very shaky on their feet can dance with their arms, heads, torsos, and legs, while sitting in their chairs.

Again let the music play for about five minutes and then have everyone sit down and share their experiences. Most often, after *imagining* themselves dancing with greater freedom, they actually *can* move with greater range than usual.

Going Places

In this imagery exercise, the leader can take the group on an imaginary trip to a place of his or her choice, such as a beach, a forest, or an island paradise. My choice is the beach, and I use a tape of ocean sounds to accompany me.

I begin by asking everyone to close their eyes and, after taking a few deep breaths, to relax. Or, I might lead the group through one of the relaxations. Then I ask them to imagine themselves on a beach. I ask them to tune into all of their senses.

I say: "Hear the sound of the ocean and smell the salt air. See the sun in a fair blue sky and feel the warmth of the sun on your body. See and feel yourself lying on the beach; feel the impression your body is making in the sand; feel the weight of your body in the sand. You may even hear a few sea gulls. Envision the edge of the ocean, see the little wave that trickles onto the beach and glistens like gems in the sun.

"Slowly allow yourself to be carried out into a calm

sea, smelling the salt air even more strongly because you are so close to it, almost tasting it. As your body floats, feel the coolness of the water under you and the warmth of the sun above you, feeling the coolness even more as the water splashes on the front of your body every now and then. Feel the undulation of the water under you as you continue to float, being aware of the difference that your body feels between floating and the weightedness of lying in the sand."

I allow a little time between each suggestion (10 to 20 seconds) so that the group can first see and then feel these images.

I then continue, "Now let your mind's eye go to the sky and pick out one puffy cloud in a relatively clear blue sky. This will be your companion cloud. Allow your body to slowly float up next to this cloud and feel the freedom of floating in the air. Feel the breezes and be aware of the different feeling between floating in the air and floating on the water." Then I slowly bring the group back to the reality of the moment and ask if anyone would like to share what they felt and how they feel now.

This imagery can be followed by a drawing session, letting everyone draw the images they saw.

Your Own Place

After leading the group through one of the relaxations, tell them at the count of three to picture themselves in their favorite place of relaxation, either a place they have been to before, indoors or out, or a place they can make up in their own minds. Tell them when they get to this place they should tune into all their senses: seeing, hearing, smelling, and feeling everything in their chosen surroundings.

If it's indoors, ask them to be aware of what colors are there, where the furniture is, what is on the walls, and what sounds and smells are there. Ask: "Is what you are sitting or standing on soft or hard? Are you alone?" If they are outdoors, ask them to go through the same process with their senses. Then count to three and snap your fingers, saying: "You are now there. See, hear, smell, feel, and taste, if that applies." Tell everyone to take about 30 secnds to get accustomed to this place. Ask them to choose a word, such as Love, Peace, Calm, Clarity, or any other word they would like. Tell them: "When you have your word, feel this word and its meaning throughout your whole body, in every pore of your being. You now are this word. If you word is 'Love,' you are love. Love radiates from you and anyone who comes near you becomes love with you."

Remind the group, "This word is yours and you can call upon it anytime you'd like. You just have to close your eyes, take a few slow deep breaths, count to three, and the feeling is yours again. You own it."

Slowly bring the group back to reality and allow time for sharing and discussion.

Inner Guide

Ask the group to close their eyes and take a few slow and deep breaths, relaxing and letting go of their bodies and minds. Then tell them they are going to go on a journey. Each person should think of a question they want answered, or a problem they want help with. Now ask each person to envision going through a door opening out to a path that goes up a mountain on a beautiful spring day. "Feel the breezes and smell the fresh mountain air.

"As you walk, you will pass lovely trees and plants, some with fragrant scents. You may even decide to pause and bend down to smell or pick a flower or two. As you continue up this path you may see squirrels, rabbits, or other playful creatures of nature. A little further up the mountain you will come to a bubbling brook and you may want to stop to take a drink, or run your finger through the water. You may even decide to rest, to take off your shoes and dangle your feet in the water.

"At your own pace, you may continue when you please on your way up the path. Further along the path you will encounter your guide. This guide may be in any shape or form, human or otherwise. When you do meet your guide, start a conversation. Get to know your guide and then ask your question." (Allow about one minute for each to start this conversation.) When you have concluded your encounter, say your farewells. Know that you can meet again whenever you choose, and slowly return down the path and back through the door."

Give everyone a few minutes and then remind them that, if they haven't already started their journeys back, it is now time to do so. You may want to lead them back, or allow them to return on their own.

It is a good idea to have a sharing discussion when the group is ready. There may be some people who did not meet their guide. Assure them that it can happen that way, and that perhaps next time they will.

Alice in Wonderland

This is a visualization that can help place a specific relationship into a different perspective. Have each person think of a close relationship they have with someone like a mate, child, close friend or, if in a retirement home or nursing home, a nurse or caregiver. Then ask everyone to close their eyes, take a few slow and deep breaths and let go, relaxing body and mind.

Lead into this imagery by saying: "Imagine yourself with this person you have chosen, and picture where you are, indoors or outdoors. If indoors, which room are you sitting in? Is it at a table, or on a sofa, or other setting? If outdoors, are you on a patio, a lawn, a beach? Where are you sitting? When you have decided where you are, see yourself and your partner in this place, and start an imaginary conversation."

Give the group a few moments to establish this conversation in their mind's eye and then continue: "You will notice that a bottle will appear in your right hand. On this bottle is a tag that will say 'Drink me' and, like Alice in Wonderland, you will drink the contents of this bottle, and you will begin to become very small; as small as Tom Thumb, as small as a thimble. But you will continue having a conversation with this person, whose size does not change, noticing how you feel physically and emotionally. How does it feel to be so small, so tiny? How does your body feel? How do you feel in the environment, the furniture? Does your conversation change? How is your partner treating you, and how are you relating to and responding to this person?"

Allow a few moments for this scenario to develop. Then continue: "Now you will notice that a bottle has appeared in your left hand and a tag on this bottle reads, 'Drink me.' You drink the contents of this bottle and, like Alice in Wonderland, you find yourself growing larger and larger until you are giant size, filling the entire room you are in, with your head touching the ceiling, unless you are outside. Your partner, meanwhile, has remained the same size, and your conversation has continued. Again, be aware of how you feel being so large, towering over the person you are with. How does your body feel, your clothes, the furniture, and how do you feel emotionally? Has your conversation changed? How are you relating now? How is this person treating you, and how are you treating this person?"

Allow a few moments for this scenario to be established and then continue. "At this point another bottle will appear in your hand and it too will have a tag on it that says, 'Drink me.' You will drink the contents of this bottle and then find yourself shrinking back to your normal size. Your partner and you will continue to talk while this is happening and, when you reach your normal size, you will find a way to complete your conversation. Slowly open your eyes and return with the group."

Follow this with a sharing discussion. Ask what each person learned about themselves and their relationship with the person they had chosen. Ask, "When you became small, did you feel vulnerable or frightened or were you carefree and playful? Did the person you were with take care of you, baby you, protect you, or take advantage of you and bully you or patronize you? When you become enormous, did your partner cower, or treat you with more respect?" Use the discussion time to be a time to recognize, vent, and share feelings.

THE IMPORTANCE OF TOUCH

"The raw sensation of touch as stimulus is vitally necessary for the physical survival of the organism . . . The need for tactile stimulation must be added to the repertoire of basic needs in all vertebrates. . ."[17]

Touching, in our culture, is intimidating to some; yet it is very important. The opportunity to touch and be touched is often lacking in the lives of older adults. Some may no longer have a spouse, and many have minimal or no contact with young children who are wonderful about unself-consciously climbing on your lap and putting their arms around you. The skin is the largest sense organ we have, and is the "prime organ of relation to the outside."[18]

After a class has been meeting for awhile and I feel confident that they would be comfortable with touch, I introduce some hands-on experiences. I end all my classes with shared hugs, sometimes waiting until after a few initial meetings with a new class. Therefore, by the time I present hands-on activities, everyone has already touched. It is important from the beginning to establish a safe environment where everyone feels secure in the fact that they have permission to be comfortable with themselves and the group.

Those with arthritis may not be able to tolerate touch. Since the very frail are not mobile enough to participate, I sometimes go to each person and do a personal hands-on. It is a good idea to preface the activity by mentioning that those who wish not to take part do not have to. I have found the hands-on activities to be one of the favorites in every group and they are often requested. Many are amazed at the warmth they can feel from the hands, and often feel better afterwards. There is a natural healing power in the exchange and the warmth of touch.

According to an article titled "The Experience of Touch: Research Points To A Critical Role" by Daniel Goleman of *The New York Times* (February 2, 1988), it was theorized by Dr. Seymour Levine from Stanford University Medical School, that in humans a touch-induced reduction of stress hormones may account for the soothing effects of skin-to-skin contact.

In his book, *Living, Loving & Learning,* Leo Buscaglia quotes Dr. Harold Falk, senior psychiatrist at the Menninger Foundation: "Hugging can lift depression, enabling the body's immunization system to become tuned up. Hugging breathes fresh life into tired bodies and makes you feel younger and more vibrant. In the home, hugging can strengthen relationships and significantly reduce tensions." Buscaglia further states, "Helen Colton in her book, *Joy of Touching,* said that the hemoglobin in the blood increases significantly when you are touched . . . Hemoglobin is that part of the blood that carries the vital supplies of oxygen to the heart and to the brain—and she says that if you want to be healty, you must touch each other, you must love each other, you must hold each other."

Hands-On

Tell the members of the group to find a partner and move their chairs so that they are facing each other. Then tell them: "Close your eyes, place your own hands together, and rub them. As you breathe deeply, mentally focus your breath into your hands. Now, with eyes open, place your hands (fingers and thumbs up) on your partner's hands. Once again close your eyes. Breathe deeply and focus your mind on the hands. Feel the warmth. Very slowly lessen the pressure so that you are barely touching, yet continue to feel the warmth. Now, with eyes open or closed, move your hands a fraction of an inch away and then touch again. Continue to do this and move further and further, going forward and touching and then away again, to and fro, like a magnet. See how far you can go and still feel the heat of your partner's hands."

Shoulders

Tell the group: "Partner up. One sit and the other stand behind the partner's chair. The person sitting should close your eyes and take a few deep breaths; relax. The person standing should place your hands together as in the previous activity.

"Before placing your hands on your partner, you may want to tune in to a higher consciousness and ask to be a channel for healing. You may also want to focus on love and positive thoughts.

"After you have taken a few deep breaths, place your hands gently on top of your partner's shoulders, close to the neck. Just let the warmth of your hands feel the warmth of your partner's shoulders as you both focus on this area and do some deep, relaxed breathing. Gently squeeze your hands, so that you are squeezing the shoulder area. Slowly continue this movement while you move your hands out-

Figure 9-1   Hands-On

ward toward the edge of the shoulder and back again toward the neck. The sitting partner is free to express pref-
erence for a firmer or a gentler touch.

"Next, the standing partner can make circles with the
thumb, gently massaging along the shoulder area and fin-
ishing with still and quiet hands, as when you started. Both
take a few deep breaths and then brush your hands gently
outward along your partner's shoulders as if you were
brushing off some lint. End by shaking out your hands.
Change places with your partner and repeat the whole
process."

The above hands-on activity can be extended by having
the seated person bend his torso forward so that the partner can reach the shoulder blades and more of the spine.
Tell the massaging persons that they can gently run their
fingers along the inside of the shoulder blades next to the
spine, just off the bone where all the muscles are attached.

Small circular motions along this line can release tension and will feel good.

After placing either the thumbs or the first two fingers of each hand at the very top of the neck, one hand on each side of the spine, tell the givers: "Once again make small circles all the way down the spine as far as the waist, or as far down as can comfortably be reached." This is where the muscles are attached. As a result, the exercise can ease tautness and impart a relaxed feeling.

Always end this hands-on exercise with the receiver in an upright position in the chair and the giver (massager) placing the hands in the starting position on the shoulders near the neck, while both focus on their breath, the stillness of the hands, and the warmth of the connection between the hands and the shoulders.

Hands

Tell the group to face a partner, both in chairs, and to take turns gently massaging each other's hands. Tell them: "Take the time to do each and every finger. Place a finger and thumb on the top and bottom of each knuckle, making circles to the fingertip. Then place a finger and thumb on the sides of each finger, making circles to the fingertip. Try stretching the fingers back gently, then pulling each finger gently. Be sure to massage the palms and the top of the hands between the bones. Finish by gently stretching each hand from the wrist, up and down, as if you were waving hello. Now, without forcing, circle the hand from the wrist in both directions. Then hold the hand between your two hands, again focusing on breath and warmth."

Polarity

Another healing hands-on activity uses the warmth of your hands on different places on the body at the same time. This can be done on your own body, or with a partner.

Tell the group to place a part of the body that is tense or in pain in between their right and left hands. An example would be to place the right hand on the front of a knee and the left hand on back of the knee.

You can have the class experiment by each taking a partner and practicing on an arm, leg, shoulder, or even the head. Have the givers rub their palms together to cause friction and warmth, as in the first hands-on activity. After placing the hands in a polarity position (one front and one back on a knee, or one top and one bottom on an arm, or on either side, as at the temples of a head), ask everyone to close their eyes and focus on their breathing and the connection between the hands. This often is felt as a healing energy. Be sure everyone has a turn at being both the giver and the receiver.

After any hands-on activity, I remind the class that it is a good idea to wash their hands after the class. This is a good idea in any case, since many of the classes take place before a meal.

Chapter 10

CHAIR EXERCISES AND SAMPLE CLASS

A physical fitness class includes exercises for articulation of joints, flexibility, balance, and strength. Because exercise increases breathing, it supplies needed oxygen to the brain which, in turn, serves to maintain mental alertness in the aging adult. A staff member at a retirement home where I worked commented after seeing photos taken during a More Than Movement class: "It is so nice to see the residents looking so alert; usually they aren't."

SAMPLE CLASS

I design my classes so that fitness is fun. It is a good idea to remind everyone: "Always listen to your own body, it is your best teacher. Do not do anything that gives you pain, no matter what I or anyone else tells you. Find your own limits."

Whenever possible, I have the chairs arranged in a

circle. I begin every class by greeting each person in a coming together activity, such as passing a musical instrument around for each person to play and then having them say their name. Or, I go to each person myself and take his or her hands in mine, look into his or her eyes and say, "Hello, *Emma,* I'm glad you're here."

Breathing

Next, I do something that will deepen breathing, stretching the diaphragm and the rest of the body slowly and gently. I tell them: "Take a deep breath and stretch your arms and head as far back as you can. Exhale and reach for your toes, or as far down as you can. Do it four times. Now take a deep breath, reach for the ceiling and, as you exhale, drop your arms and say, 'Ha, ha, ha, ha, ha' as loud as you can to stimulate your diaphragm. Repeat this process, saying, 'He, he, he, he, he' and then, 'She, she, she, she, she,' and lastly, 'Ho, ho, ho, ho, ho.' On the last one, place your hands on your rib cage, feeling the expansion as you breath in; and as you breath out, feel the rib cage contract." Some may not know where their rib cage is, so you will have to demonstrate or actually place their hands there for them. This is another good time to present the skeleton.

Use recordings of ocean sounds or any other gentle music for the breathing exercises. Change the music for the following exercises to something with a slow and easy beat, such as a blues, ragtime, or a slow disco.

After the breathing exercises, I initiate the part of the class that focuses on body-part-by-part warm-up. This is either presented in a structured way or by using a creative activity, such as a category dance or non-locomotor movements. These are some of the exercises I use.

Head

"Slowly and gently bring your chin down as far as you can and as close to the chest as possible, then lift your head up, focusing your eyes to the ceiling. Repeat this four times. Now let your ear drop to one shoulder, being careful not to lift your shoulders. Gently stretch your neck from side to side as if you have heavy earrings in your ears. Repeat four times. Now circle your head four times to one side and four times to the other side. Imagine your nose or your chin drawing as large a circle as possible in the air. Or, imagine a beam of light shining out of the top of your head and shine the beam of light around in an enormous circle. You may hear a sound like Rice Krispies as you hear your neck snap, crackle, and pop. When doing the circling, keep your eyes open to keep from getting dizzy."

There is some controversy about making complete circles with the head. It is my belief that each person needs to feel this out for one's self. "Remember you are your *own* teacher—the teacher leading the class is only a guide who you do *not* have to follow. Learn to pay closer attention to what your own body tells you."

Shoulders

"Lift your shoulders up as high as you can and press them down as far as you can, twice. Stretch them forward and backward twice. Now place your hands on your shoulders and elbows out to the side and aim them front and back, trying to touch them together in the front. Then stretch them back as far as you can. Do this twice slowly and four times quickly. With hands still on your shoulders, aim your elbows out to the side and move them up and down four times slowly and four times quickly. Follow by drawing large circles in the air with the elbows four times in one direction and four times in the opposite direction. Keeping your hands on your shoulders, now try to place both elbows on one leg and then the other, stretching and twisting the spine. Aim to reach as close to your hip as you can and do this four times to each side."

Fingers and Hands

"Stretch your fingers out as wide as you can. Make tight fists; shake them like pepper shakers and throw them away, stretching your fingers out as you do so. Repeat four times. Now wiggle all your fingers as if you were playing a piano; now wiggle them like you are typing or playing a banjo. Keep wiggling the fingers as you reach up high above your head, under your chair, or as close to the floor as you can. Wiggle the fingers of both hands on one side of your chair and then the other side; behind your neck; behind your back. Keep wiggling the fingers as you stretch your arms open wide, then cross them over your chest and give yourself a hug.

"With both hands, at the same time touch one finger at a time to the thumbs of the same hands—first your pointing fingers, then your middle fingers, next your ring fingers and last your little fingers. Repeat this process four to six times, doing it a little faster each time. Then shake out your hands and circle your wrists four times in each direction."

Side Stretches

"Lift your left arm over your head, keeping it near your ear. Take a deep breath and let it out as you reach over your head like a rainbow or an arch towards your right side, reaching with as straight an elbow as you can toward your neighbor and stretching your torso. Come to center, change arms, take a deep breath, and repeat to the

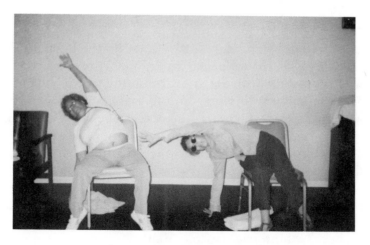

Figure 10-1   Side Stretches

other side. Continue changing sides until you have done three or four of these curved stretches to each side."

Reaching and Bending

This exercise strengthens the stomach and stretches the side muscles helping to tone up the waistline. "Reach up with both arms as high as you can, stretching the elbows as straight as you can, then reach down as low as you can, aiming to touch your toes or the floor. Do eight sets at a fairly quick pace. Then reach as far as you can to the left and up in front with both arms, and then aim for the floor on your right, doing four sets. Imagine reaching high up on a top shelf for a blanket or an old photo album, then placing it on the floor next to the chair. Repeat four sets reaching up tall on the right and touching down low on the left."

Arm Exercises, Seated

"Imitate swimming strokes. First do the breaststroke, reaching forward with each arm as far front as you can as well as reaching with the upper torso and turning the head as if you were swimming. Do this eight times." For those who never learned how to swim, this can be like a swimming lesson. You can tell everyone to imagine that they are in a race across the English Channel. Jokingly remind them that it is much easier without water.

"Next try the backstroke, letting the head and eyes follow each arm as it circles back." In some nursing homes the couches or the chairs do not permit this kind of movement. The butterfly stroke is another arm movement that uses both arms at the same time. "Placing the backs of both hands together, palms out, thumbs down, reach both arms forward and out from the chest as far as you can before opening the arms out and around to the side; then start again. Repeat eight times."

Other arm movements can include some basic calisthenics such as: "Place the hands on the shoulders, reaching them up in the air, and then return them to the shoulders. Repeat this eight times and then do eight sets of reaching out to the side and back in to the shoulders. Now reach down with the arms and return to the shoulders eight times."

I also like to include graceful balletlike arm movements using music such as waltzes. "Opening the arms to the side, allow one arm at a time to reach over your head towards the other arm and back out again with the torso following. Alternating arms, do this eight times. Repeat by reaching each arm across the body towards the other arm, letting the head and eyes follow the moving arm. Again, alternate arms and do eight times. Then swing both arms over the head from one side to the other like a willow tree, eight times. Next, starting on your right side, let both arms swing around front and to the left side, going from side to side, following the arms with the head and eyes."

End the balletlike arm series by circling arms. "With the arms open to the side, level with the shoulders, circle them down, crossing them as they lift, up and out to the side eight times, making the circle as big as you can. Then reverse the circle and end with the arms crossed on top of the legs." This series of exercises makes use of the arms as much as calisthenics, but gives a sense of rhythm, dance, and flow.

Churning Butter

This is particularly good for those who cannot stand, but is beneficial for everyone. It gives them a chance to use their torso and hips. "Use the image of churning butter as you make large circles of the torso as if your head and torso were a stick, and attempt to lift each hip and buttock as the body moves around, reaching your chest as close to your legs as you can.

Standing and Sitting

This method of standing up makes use of gravity to make standing and sitting easier. "Start in a sitting position. Place one foot in front of the other; hold onto the sides of your chair and lean your body weight forward, letting gravity help you. Push your feet against the floor and your hands on the chair as you aim forward and up. Practice this process a few times, reversing it to sit." This itself is a good exercise.

STANDING EXERCISES

In a group with mixed abilities, for those who can't stand, offer an alternative exercise to the ones that can't be done in a sitting position.

More Arm Exercises

"In a standing position all facing the center of the circle, place your right arms[19] forward, keeping the elbow straight. Slowly move your arm front, up and back as far as you can, and then down, making a large circle that starts from the shoulder, not the elbow. Slowly repeat this twice, a bit faster, and then eight times spinning your arms like a windmill or a propeller. Repeat with the left arm.

"Now turn sideways, so that you don't hit anyone when moving your arms. Reach your arms out to the side and down and cross them as they reach up, twice slowly, twice a bit faster, and then eight times as fast as you can, circling your arms down, up and around.

"Face center again. Lift your arms, bent at the elbows, chest-high, pointing the fingers of both hands towards each other, palms down. Quickly pull the elbows back toward the shoulder blades, back of you, and release them back to starting position, eight times." This develops the pectoral muscles.

Push-ups Against a Wall

These are good for the backs of the upper arms (triceps), the part of the arms that tends to be flabby.

"Place your hands on the wall chest high, fingers facing each other. Make sure you do not lift your shoulders, and keep them as relaxed as possible. If it is too difficult to have the fingertips facing, then point your fingers toward the ceiling. Place your feet far enough away from the wall so that your body is leaning toward it at an angle. In a slow count of four, push smoothly away from the wall, and in a slow count of four come back, trying to touch your nose gently to the wall. Do not jerk or stop at each count. Be careful to move your body all at once so that your pelvis is not sticking out. Take it with you as you move. Do this

Figure 10-2   Push-ups Against a Wall

eight times, more or less, according to your strength and ability. If you need to, start with four and increase the number slowly over time. However, if you have the ability to do eight, do so and then rest, taking your arms off the wall and shaking them out. Then repeat another eight, taking one count to reach the wall and one count to push away from the wall until you have counted to sixteen, making another eight push-ups, or push-offs."

For those who can't stand, have them place their hands together, chest-high, elbows out to the sides, and press the hands together for eight counts and then release. Tell them to repeat this isometric exercise four to eight times.

Knee Bends and Metatarsal Stretches

"If necessary, hold onto the back of your chair with one or two hands. Place feet about 6 to 12 inches apart, keeping your toes forward and feet parallel. Bend your knees, being careful to aim them directly over your toes. If you turn your knees in or too far out beyond the toes, you may injure them. Be aware of this whenever you bend your knees. Bend and straighten your knees eight times. Then lift your heels off the ground, standing on the balls of your feet. Be careful not to turn your ankles. Move your body straight up, just as if a marionette string were attached to the top of your head and being lifted to the ceiling right above you. Do not lift your shoulders. Lift and lower your heels eight times. Then alternate with bending your knees, straightening them and lifting your heels, combining the two exercises. Do this exercise in a set of eight, trying to balance on the balls of your feet for a few moments at the end. If you are holding onto a chair, try to let go and maintain your balance."

This exercise is good for strengthening calf muscles and the metatarsals, which are the arches of your feet. Those who are sitting can lift their heels on and off the floor while their feet remain in a parallel position.

Torso Swings

"Think of your spine as a maypole and your arms as the ribbons hanging from the maypole. As you bend your knees over your toes, swing your arms around your body as far to the side as you can, resulting in a gentle twist of the spine. Straighten your knees as you face forward and bend them again as your arms twist to the other side. Count a swing to both sides as one and repeat each set eight times."

Arm Reaches and Back Rolls

This can be done from a standing or sitting position. "Reach to the ceiling, with both arms, as if you are picking apples off a very high tree branch. Other images to keep

Figure 10-3   Arm Reaches and Back Rolls

in mind might include climbing a ladder or a rope. Now
reach both arms up and, with one arm at a time, stretch
as high as you can from the heels to your fingertips eight
times, keeping the elbows straight. Then let your body melt
down slowly, arms and head first in a rolling manner, vertebra by vertebra, as far down to the floor as you can, aiming to touch your toes or the floor, head down. Remain in
this position while you bend your knees and then straighten
them twice. Then bend your knees once more and roll up
your spine to a standing position, vertebra by vertebra. Repeat this series three more times. If necessary, do two sets
and then break with the next activity before repeating the
last two sets."

This exercise helps to stretch the entire body when
you are reaching and stretching, as well as the hamstrings
(the long muscles at the back of the legs) when rolling the
head down to the floor and bending and stretching the

knees. The rolling down and up helps increase articulation of the spine and torso.

Hips

"Imagine you have two strings tied to your waist, one on each side, and a ball attached to each near each hip. Hit the imaginary ball on each side twice in a set of eight and then hit each once alternating sides to the count of eight." Fast disco music helps make this exercise fun. "Follow by making a complete circle with your hips in each direction as if you were using a hula hoop." I have been told by some of my students that there used to be a dance step like this called *Messin' Around*.

"This can be followed by making figure eights with the hips in both directions, or by writing your name with your hips. Don't forget to cross the "T's" and dot the "I's." Most of the muscles in your body are attached to the top of the pelvis, called the illium crest, and most of us in this culture do not often articulate isolated movement of the pelvis.

Legs and Feet

"Stand behind your chair. Holding onto the back, open the feet out and stand with the legs far apart. Bend first one knee, keeping the heels down. Straighten and then bend the other knee. One at a time, do this eight times." This stretches the inner thigh, but may be difficult for some to do. "Be sure the knees bend out and over the toes. Proper attention to knee alignment prevents injury. If the knee is turned in or out behind the toes, there will be a strain on the knee.

"Next, bend both knees out at the same time and then straighten them. Do this eight times. Stand close to your chair and be sure that your tailbone goes straight down so that your rear end is not pointing out and away from you. When you lift up, push your feet into the floor and feel the top of your head and your whole spine lifting toward the ceiling.

"Now bring your feet together, but keep the toes turned out, heels touching. Lift first one heel off the floor, pressing into the ball of the foot, and then lower the heel. Do this four times on each foot. Follow this by rolling the foot up to where the toe is touching the floor and spring the foot off, pointing the toes down toward the floor and lifting the knee high on the side. Do this four times on each side and then repeat."

"With the toes pointing straight ahead, kick your right heel toward your buttocks, alternating four times on your right and four on your left and then repeat."

"Making sure you are far enough from furniture or people so that you have enough room, kick backwards. Alternate backward kicks, four right, four left, four right and four left.

"Follow this by placing your left hand on the back of your chair and turn your body sideways, right arm out to the side. While maintaining weight and balance on your left leg, point your right leg behind you, ready to swing your right leg front and back. Allow your leg to brush the floor as if it were a broom, and swing loosely from your hip. Count one swing front and back as one and do eight swings. Turn your body and repeat on the other side."

BACK TO SITTING

Legs

"Bring a knee up to your chest and hug the knee with both hands as close to the chest as possible. Alternating legs, do a set of eight. Repeat the set of eight, this time

Figure 10-4   Legs

aiming first your chin to each knee, then your nose, your forehead and, lastly, your right ear to your right knee and your left ear to your left knee."

This stretches your lower back and the back of the thighs.

"Lifting and holding your leg from under the thigh and near the knee, extend your leg, stretching and straightening as high as you can. Then lower the lower part of your leg, bending the leg from the knee, but keeping the thigh lifted. Extend and lower four times slowly, increasing the speed to a kick for the next four. Change legs and repeat.

"Now change legs and extend leg, pointing the heel to the ceiling, then the toes to the floor (flex and point). Do four on each leg, bending the knee after each flex and point.

"Then, to release any tension that may have built up,

Figure 10-5   Leg Lifts

do a self-massage by using the heals of your hands to rub forward four times on each thigh, like a rolling pin. Then knead each thigh like dough and pat each like a bongo drum to stimulate the skin.

"Keeping both legs extended straight out in front, point the toes down towards the floor and then back up towards your nose as far as you can. Do four sets slowly and four sets faster. Then point the toes inward towards each other and outwards to the sides, letting the heels touch—four times in and out slowly, and four times in and out faster." (I sometimes say, "Let your toes kiss and let your heels kiss.") This is followed by circling the feet so that the ankles are being articulated. "Imagine that you are drawing circles in the air with your toes, going four times in each direction.

"In chairs, march with your knees up high, doing four sets of eight.

Kicking a cookie can is an idea I got in a workshop with dance therapist Lisa Polk. Her focus was handicapped children, but I have found that every group I work with, of no matter what age or ability, find this activity a challenge, and fun. Using the bottom part of a ten-to-twelve-inch cookie can as a target to kick, I pass it around for each person to hold out in front of them and kick eight times, alternating legs. For those who have difficulty, I hold the can for them and raise or lower it accordingly. Even the very frail, with minimum movement capacity, and those who rarely participate, will want to kick the can. Having an object outside of the self often serves as an excellent motivating force. The sound of the tin as the can is being kicked adds another stimulating element. I believe this also provides a good opportunity for venting some emotions.

After everyone has had a turn, there are several variations on this I use when possible:

"Standing next to your chair, and holding on to it when necessary, kick the can eight times, alternating legs.

"Moving across the circle or the room, alternate step-kick, step-kick, eight times." With those whose balance is questionable, but who want to try, I hold onto them.

"Holding the can in your right hand, behind you and down low, try to kick it from behind you with your left foot." This requires coordination and concentration and often provokes laughter and giggles at the resulting confusion of body and mind.

Elbow to Knee Touch

"From a sitting or a standing position, bring your right elbow and your left knee together, touching if you can, and then your left elbow to your right knee, alternating eight times."

Bike Ride

"Starting with your right leg, bring your knee up and push out front with your foot, making large circles just as if you are riding a bicycle. When you have completed four circles in one direction, reverse the direction of the circle and do four more. Repeat with left leg."

Leg Lifts

"Imagine that there is a milk carton placed on the floor at the right front corner of your chair. Lift your right knee high and bring your leg over the carton, and around to the right side of your chair, onto the floor, and then, back over in front again until you have done the entire movement eight times. Then repeat this with your left leg on the left side of your chair." This exercise was suggested to me by Mary Brewster, from the retired senior volunteer program.

Mat and Floor Work

For those who have mats or are willing to use a large towel and who are able to get down on the floor, these exercises are very good for the lower back and spine. For those who have problems with their backs, these exercises also can help to strengthen and stretch the back as well as strengthen the stomach. I have included a few leg exercises as well. Because there is less effort fighting gravity when you are lying down, it often is easier to work some parts of the body from this position.

Just getting down to the floor and back up again is an exercise that is very important for the older adult who may lose the ability to do many simple movements, like getting in and out of a tub. With practice, you can strengthen the muscles required to get up and down, therefore providing more mobility.

There are times when some may want to try these exercises but are afraid to. Offering help and encouragement may change their minds. Be sure that if you offer help, you are strong enough to give support. If not, enlist the help of some other members of the group or staff. In some groups, only a few will be willing to try when you first begin floor work, but if you continue to offer the exercises, along with encouragement, more people will join in. For those who have had strokes or those who have given up trying because of other injuries or pain, getting down and back up again not only builds self-confidence and self-esteem, but gives them the courage to try other things they thought they couldn't do.

Getting Down on the Floor

"Reach for the floor with your hand and go down on one knee and then the other hand and other knee. Your chair may be used as a support if you wish. In that case,

Figure 10-6   Getting Down On The Floor - Step 1

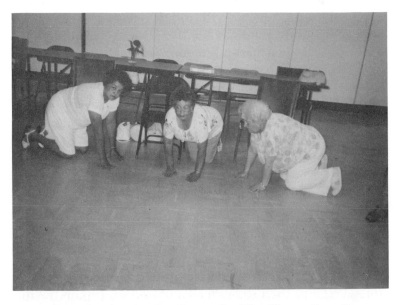

Figure 10-7   Getting Down On The Floor - Step 2

Figure 10-8   Getting Down On The Floor - Step 3

you may want to put your hand on the seat of your chair as a support, and then place your knee on the floor, followed by your other hand and other knee. Now slowly sit on one hip, slide your arm and torso down to the floor, and roll over onto your back."

Some individuals will need to have a small pillow or a rolled towel placed under their heads.

"On your back, put your feet on the floor as close to your buttocks as possible with your knees up. If you are on a mat, bring your hips as close to the edge of the mat as you can. Gently rock your pelvis back and forth, first moving towards your head and then towards your feet, trying to get your waistline closer to the floor, then relaxing and releasing it. Pushing with your feet helps. After doing this six to eight times, gently roll your pelvis up off the floor vertebra by vertebra, as far up as you can, in the direction of your shoulders (see Figure 10-9). Keep your feet

Figure 10-9   Rolling Pelvis up Vertebra by Vertebra

Figure 10-10   Knee to Chest

and knees together so that you use more of your inner thigh muscles. Roll down slowly, vertebra by vertebra, trying to place your waist down before your buttocks. Repeat four times.

"Bring your knee up to your chest and hug it with your hands at the same time that you raise your head towards your knee (see Figure 10-10). Put your head down when you place your foot on the floor close to your body and slide the foot forward, pressing your heel towards the wall in front of you. Repeat four times with each leg.

"Bring both knees up to your chest and hug them with your hands (see Figure 10-11). Repeat four times, and on the fourth time gently rock from side to side, just on either side of your spine, feeling the massage you will get from the floor or mat. If you need to, you can stop yourself with your elbows so that you don't roll all the way over. Repeat this with your head reaching toward your knees, rolling from side to side on the fourth one.

"Placing your arms straight out, one on each side, bring both of your knees to your right side, trying to keep both shoulders down on the mat. Feel the stretch in your back. Keeping your elbow as straight as you can, move your arm in large counterclockwise circles, as close to the floor as you can, across your body and over your head, following your hand with your eyes. Do this four times going up and four times going down. Repeat to the other side, bringing your knees to the left side and circling with your right arm.

"This exercise is a modified sit-up which works the psoas muscle to strengthen the stomach, thereby helping the back. Still on your back, knees up and feet on the floor, place your right ankle on top of your left knee, and let the right knee open to the side as much as you can. Slide your arms and hands forward, stretching towards your feet and slightly off the floor, and raise your head and shoulders and hold them for 10 counts and release back down to the floor slowly. If you get neck pain, keep your chin up to-

Figure 10-11   Hugging Both Knees to Chest

Figure 10-12   Modified Sit-Up

wards the ceiling rather than pointing it down into your chest. For those who can't cross the leg; Bend the knees and keep the feet on the floor close to your body and reach your hands toward your knees. It helps to breathe in slowly on the release and breathe out slowly as you reach forward. Do this four to eight times and then change legs and repeat on the other side.

"Still on your back, with your feet on the floor and the knees bent, straighten your right leg on the floor. Do eight leg lifts at your own pace with your right leg, trying to keep your leg straight. Lift the leg as high as you can and place the whole leg on the floor after each leg lift. Repeat with the other leg.

"Roll over to your right side, supporting yourself with your left hand on the floor in front of you. If it is more comfortable, bend your right leg under you. Now do eight leg lifts with your left leg, pointing the knee to the ceiling as it lifts and keeping it as straight as you can. Bend your knees and roll over to your left side and repeat this with your right leg. Roll over onto your hands and knees and come to a standing position, one foot at a time."

Using fast and upbeat music, have the class do four sets of fast walks around the room, going in any direction they please. Next, ask them to "Walk for eight counts, then bend and touch the floor." Have the class do four sets of these. The object is to get everyone moving using both walks and bends. The instructor also could make use of fast dancing or any of the creative movement activities that are relatively fast and fun.

I include one or two creative activities in each session and usually conclude with a "thought for the day" or I share an experience I believe will be interesting or relevant. I then follow with a relaxation before our hand-holding circle ends the session.

CLOSURE

As I end this book with a description of how I end my classes, I would like to invite those who want, to feel free to write me (c/o Human Sciences Press, Inc.) with any questions or comments. A video tape of the program will be available soon.

I end all of my classes where possible with a hand-holding circle, including those who have to remain in their chairs (we arrange our circle to include these chairs). I ask everyone to close their eyes and I say: "Take a deep breath all the way to your toes, filling your body with all the goodness in the world and, when you breathe out, breathe out all the garbage you no longer need—all the problems, pains, worries, fears, and negative thoughts. Breathe in all the love in the world. Open your hearts and fill your bodies with light and love. Then breathe out and share this love with everyone in this room, feeling it pass from hand to hand, round and round the circle. Now breathe in all the love in the entire universe and share it with the whole world." At first you may feel uneasy or embarrassed at saying this, but I find that all my groups enjoy this tremendously.

Sometimes I suggest that everyone imagine a person they know, who needs healing, is in the center of our circle. I ask all of them to send their love and prayers to the center of the circle.

I also may ask everyone to open their eyes and make loving eye contact with each person in the circle.

I always end with everyone giving each other hugs. With immobile people, I go to each and share a hug. I tell everyone I am a collector of hugs. When someone says, "I only have one arm to hug you with," I tell them, "All the love you need can come through one arm."

When I hug, I try to hug honestly, with warmth, feeling love from my heart. After being hugged by me, one woman at a retirement home said, "I haven't had a real hug in such a long time." After my first time at a recreation center, someone asked if I had been there before because I seemed to know them; I seemed familiar. Because I look for the goodness and the light within each person, there is a familiarity and a connectedness I project.

With the very frail I go to each, ask if they have a hug for me, then take their hands, look into their eyes and say, "Thank you for being here and I'll see you next class" (I state the day), and then I say, "God Bless You."

BIBLIOGRAPHY

Aging Newwork News, *Spirituality and Aging: Fostering Spiritual Well-Being of the Older Adult,* Dec., 1986.

American Association of Retired Persons, *Truth About Aging, Guidelines for Accurate Communication,* 1984.

Brooks, Charles V. W. *Sensory Awareness: The Rediscovery of Experiencing.* N.Y.; Viking Press, 1974.

Bry, Adeleaide. *Visualization.* N.Y.: Harper & Row, 1979.

Buscaglia, Leo. *Living, Loving & Learning.* N.Y.: Holt & Co., 1982.

Casper, Ursula Hodge. *Joy and Comfort through Stretching and Relaxing For Those Who Are Unable To Exercise.* Toronto, Canada: Image Publishing, Inc. 1982.

Dass, Ram & Gorman, Paul. *How Can I Help?* N.Y.: Alfred A. Knopf, 1987.

Davis, Flora. *Inside Intuition.* New York: Signet Paperback, The New American Library, Inc., 1971.

Dell, Cecily. *A Primer for Movement Description Using Effort/Shape & Supplementary Concept.* New York: Dance Notation Bureau, Inc., 1970.

Fast, Julius. *Body Language.* New York: M. Evans & Co., Inc., 1970.

Gawain, Shakti. *Creative Visualization.* New York: Bantam Books, 1979.

Goleman, Daniel. "The Experience of Touch: Research Points to a Critical Role." New York Times, Feb. 2, 1988.

Grams, Armin. "Overcoming Barriers to Creativity In Old Age." *Perspective On Aging,* The National Council on the Aging, Inc. Jan./Feb., 1986.

Koch, Kenneth. *I Never Told Anybody: Teaching Poetry Writing In A Nursing Home.* New York: Vintage Books, 1977.

Lerman, Liz. *Teaching Dance to Senior Adults.* Springfield, Ill.: Charles C. Thomas, Inc. 1984.

Levine, Stephen. *Who Dies? An Investigation of Conscious Living and Conscious Dying.* New York: Anchor Books, 1982.

Lowen, Alexander. *Bioenergetics.* New York: Penguin Books, 1975.

Maas, H. J. and Kuypers, A. *From Thirty to Seventy: A Forty-year Longitudinal Study of Adult Life Styles and Personality.* San Francisco: Josey-Bass, 1974.

Manheimer, Director, NCOA's Humanities Program, "Creative Arts: A Threshold To Renewed Life." *Perspective On Aging,* NCOA, Jan./Feb., 1986.

Montagu, Ashley. *Touching, The Human Significance of the Skin.* New York: Harper & Row, 1971.

Murray, Ruth L. *Dance in Elementary Education* (2nd ed.). New York: Harper & Row, 1963.

Painter, Charlotte, text and Valois, Photography. *Gifts of Age.* San Francisco: Chronicle Books, 1985.

Shorr, Joseph. *Go See the Movie In Your Head.* Santa Barbara, Ca: Ross Erikson.

Siegal, Bernie S. M. D. *Love, Medicine and Miracles.* New York: Harper & Row, 1988.

Simonton, O. Carl, M. D., Matthews-Somonton, Stephanie and Creighton, James L. *Getting Well Again.* New York: Bantom Books, 1978.

Switkes, Betty. *Senior-cize: Exercises and Dances in a Chair.* Washington, D.C.: Senior-cize, 1982.

FOOTNOTES

1. *Spirituality and Aging: Fostering Spiritual Well-Being of the Older Adult,* Aging Network News, Dec., 1986.

2. Ibid. p. 6.

3. For further ideas, see Ruth L. Murray, *Dance in Elementary Education,* Harper & Row, 1953.

4. *A Primer for Movement Description Using Effort/Shape & Supplementary Concept,* Cecily Dell, Dance Notation Bureau, Inc., New York, 1970.

5. *Kitaro* Silk Road II, 1985 Canyon Records, Japan, GramaVision/ Gravity Records, New York, KM 18-7011-1.

6. "Grandma's Hands," *Bill Withers at Carnegie Hall,* Sussex Label #SXB5-7025-2, 2-record set, side one.

7. ibid. Side One.

8. *Bill Withers Making Music,* Columbia PO33704, Side One.

9. Nadine Wobus, music therapist, gave me this idea.

10. Grams, Armin, in *Perspective on Aging,* Jan./Feb. 1986, The National Council on the Aging, Inc.

11. Maas, H. J. and Kuypers, A. *From Thirty to Seventy: A Forty-year Longitudinal Study of Adult Life Styles and Personality.* San Francisco: Josey-Bass, 1974.

12. Manheimer, Director, NCOA's Humanities Program, "Creative Arts: A Threshold to Renewed Life" in *Perspective on Aging*, NCOA, Jan./Feb., 1986.

13. A relaxation audio tape containing this exercise is available for sale. A Moving Experience, 1884 Columbia Rd., N.W., #105, Wash., D.C. 20009, $10.

14. Steve Halpern's music such as the Spectrum Suite, HS 770, Halpern Sounds, P.O. Box 720, Palo Alto, CA 94302.

15. *Paul Horn Inside 11*, KE31600, Vancouver Island Productions, Ltd.

16. *Jean Michel Jarre Equinoxe*, 1978, Francis Dreyfus Music, 26, Ave. Kleber, 75116, Paris.

17. *Touching: The Human Significance of the Skin*, Ashley Montagu, Perennial Library Paperback, Harper & Row, 1971.

18. ibid.

19. For some, left/right differentiation is difficult, so you may use this to help increase awareness and memory, or you may just say, "Place one hand. . . ."

INDEX